automatic process control

automatic process control

Ernest F. Johnson
Professor of Chemical Engineering
Princeton University

MCGRAW-HILL BOOK COMPANY
new york   st. louis   san francisco   toronto   sydney   london

To Ruth

Automatic Process Control

preface

In recent years many new books have been published dealing with various aspects of automatic control, but only a very small fraction of these have dealt wholly or in part with process control.

This book is a brief and elementary introduction to the important principles involved in the design and analysis of systems for controlling chemical and related processes. The material in the book has been used over a number of years in a one-term senior course for chemical engineers and in industrial classes with students of more diverse backgrounds.

The intention is to chart a middle-of-the-road course between a completely general and rigorous theoretical treatment, on the one hand, and a detailed treatment of specific process systems and the instruments used to control them, on the other. Highly general theoretical treatments may be interesting exercises in mathematics, but they can be sterile for engineers if they do not lead naturally to useful application. On the other hand, excessive preoccupation with specific systems leads to treatments which may be more descriptive than quantitative and which may quickly become obsolete.

A sound theoretical knowledge is an essential tool for the young engineer; indeed, it is his principal tool until he gains experience. Although no book can provide experience, it can help make theory useful.

In this book the principal technical handle is frequency-response analysis, including the damped frequency response, although some other techniques are introduced, and some of them are described in detail. A descriptive delineation of the design of a control system using the frequency response is given in Chapter 2 to orient the reader and provide a rationale for the organization of the remaining chapters.

Chapter 1 identifies the role of automatic control in process engineering and the essential characteristics of control systems. Chapters 3 to 7 describe the properties of the typical elements that comprise process control loops. Chapter 8 treats closed-loop systems, and the last two chapters are concerned with the design of simple and complex control systems.

In general, the progression through the chapters is from the simple to the complex. It is assumed that the reader has had mathematics through the calculus and some exposure to chemical engineering principles.

The examples and problem sets are important parts of the book, and are designed to be didactic. Both analog and digital machine computation are useful in solving control problems. This usefulness is pointed out in the text, but the treatment throughout is not dependent on the availability of either kind of machine.

Current trends in the field are identified principally in Chapter 10, and the selected bibliography following that chapter includes useful references for these trends and for important topics which lie outside of the scope of this book. The literature now available on control is so voluminous that only a suggestive bibliography can be included. All references cited in the text are included in the bibliography, identified by author rather than by number.

I shall not attempt to name the many generations of students and the academic and industrial colleagues who have contributed to this book. Theirs is the credit for much that is good, mine the blame for anything that is not.

Ernest F. Johnson

contents

chapter 3.   Process Dynamics.   28

chapter 4.   Distributed-parameter Process Elements.   *83*

chapter 5.   Measurement and Signal Transmission.   *101*

chapter 6.   Controllers and Control Action.   *127*

x   *Contents*

chapter 7.   Final Control Elements.   *149*

chapter 8.   Dynamics of Closed-loop Systems.   *160*

chapter 9. Design of Simple Control Systems. *217*

chapter 10.   Complex Control Systems.   *243*

nomenclature

a	constant, real part of complex numbers
A	constant, area, amplitude
b	constant, imaginary part of complex number
B	constant, transformed feedback signal
c	controlled variable
C	transformed controlled variable, capacity, capacitance
d	differential operator, diameter
D	derivative action
e	base of natural logarithms
E	voltage, transformed error signal or deviation
f	function, frequency in cycles/time
F	transformed function
G	transfer function
h	surface coefficient for heat transfer
H	feedback transfer function, hold-element transfer function
I	integral control
Im	imaginary operator
j	$\sqrt{-1}$
k	constant
K	constant, steady-state gain
l	distance
L	log modulus in decibels, Laplacian operator
m	manipulated variable, mass
M	transformed manipulated variable, closed-loop magnitude ratio
MR	magnitude ratio
MW	molecular weight
n	real number
p	polynomial function, pressure, negative pole in factored transfer function
P	transformed polynomial, proportional control
q	volumetric flow rate, polynomial function
r	reference signal, resistance
R	transform of reference signal, resistance, gas-law constant
Re	real operator
s	Laplacian complex variable, root of polynomial (with subscript)

S	slope of signature curve
t	time
T	time constant, temperature, time interval, sampling interval
u	disturbance signal
u_0	unit impulse
u_1	unit step
U	transformed disturbance signal
v	velocity
V	volume
x	process variable; input, or forcing, signal
X	transformed process variable or input signal
y	process variable; output, or response, signal
Y	transformed process variable or output signal
z	distance, position, negative zero in factored transfer function, e^{sT}

α	damping factor
β	damped frequency
γ	real number
∂	partial-differentiation operator
Δ	finite-difference operator
ζ	damping ratio
θ	angle
π	pi, 3.14 $\cdots$
ρ	density
σ	real part of exponential coefficient
Σ	summation
ϕ	angle
ψ	phase shift, phase angle, or angular displacement, radians
ω	angular frequency, rad/time
Ω	normalized frequency, ω/ω_n

Subscripts

a	ambient
A	species A
c	controller
CF	feedforward controller
d	delay, dead time
f	frictional
F	feedforward sensor
fn	flapper nozzle
i	ith, indicated, inlet, intermediate
I	integral

j	jth
m	maximum
n	nth, natural
0	outlet, critical
p	constant pressure, peak
P	proportional
r	resonant, rise, reference
s	steady state, settling
t	transient
w	wall

Superscript

*	sampled function

one
introduction

This introductory chapter is concerned with the relation of automatic control to process engineering, the nature of control, and the essential characteristics of control systems.

1-1 Basic concepts in process engineering

The process engineer (chemical engineer) is involved in the development, design, and operation of process plants. Whether he is specifically concerned with analysis or design in his technical work, he makes use of five basic concepts drawn from three major bodies of knowledge.

These basic concepts are *state, equilibrium, conservation, rate process,* and *control*. Each concept underlies a unique question which must be answered in the course of solving process problems. These questions are, respectively:

What system is involved?

What limits and constraints are imposed on the processes taking place within the system?

What amounts of material, energy, or money are involved?

What kinds and sizes of apparatus are involved?

What is the operating performance of the process system?

1-2   State

The question of identification of the system involves the thermodynamic principle of state, according to which all the properties of a system are fixed when a certain few properties are fixed. This principle seems so obvious that it is usually taken for granted, but on it depends the important fact that only a few characteristics entirely define the system. The familiar phase rule of Willard Gibbs, for example, derives directly from the principle of state.

1-3   Equilibrium

Processes cannot be carried beyond the limits of thermodynamic equilibrium; hence these limits fix the possible ranges of chemical and physical conditions for the processes taking place in the system.

1-4   Conservation

The question relating to conservation has to do with gross amounts of various quantities, and accounting procedures must be used to keep track of them. These accountings require that certain quantities be conserved in the process. The conservation of mass permits the use of the mass balance; the conservation of energy, the use of the energy balance; and the conservation of dollars in an economic study, the economic balance.

The basic ideas of state, equilibrium, and conservation derive from *thermodynamics*. Conservation, as it relates to money, derives from *economics*.

1-5 *Rate process*

The kinds and sizes of process equipment required in the system depend in part on the amounts of throughput, but also on the rates at which physical, chemical, and nuclear processes take place within the equipment. Rate processes are comprised in the field of *kinetics*.

1-6 *Control*

It is possible for a process to be feasible both thermodynamically and kinetically but inoperable because of poor operating performance either because the process is uncontrollable or because it is uneconomic. Thus the basic concepts of control in a physical sense and control in an economic sense, which underlie the question of operating performance, are as important to the design and analysis of commercially successful process systems as the concepts of equilibrium and rate process. The broad area of knowledge which includes all aspects of control may be designated *cybernetics*, following the suggestions of Ampère, Wiener, and others. Modern chemical engineering, then, is based on thermodynamics, kinetics, and cybernetics, and the last is not the least of these.

Cybernetics, in the broadest commercial sense, includes the control of physical and chemical systems and the control and management of business, which is the subject of economics. In this book we are concerned primarily with the former.

1-7 *Definition of control*

Control is the organization of activity for some purpose. Process control is the regulation of processes, usually for the immediate purpose of holding certain important process variables constant in time. It is *manual process control* when human operators do the regulating; it is *automatic process control* when machines do the regulating.

1-8 *Characteristics of control systems*

A control system is merely the controlled part of the material universe which is under consideration. Control systems have been in existence ever since the origin of life. They embrace a bewildering variety of entities, including living organisms, chemical plants, automobiles, industrial corporations, and political states, to name but a few.

Regardless of the great variety of types of control systems, they all have certain common characteristics. We describe these characteristics briefly in this section and then in somewhat greater detail in subsequent sections of this chapter. The rest of the book gives a detailed elaboration.

First, all control systems are *dynamic systems;* that is, they change in time, and it is their temporal behavior that is the important index of performance.

Second, they may all be regarded as *information-processing systems.* They all receive information, digest information, act on information, and generate information as signals of various kinds. Just as the process flow sheet traces the significant flows of material and energy in process analyses, so does the signal-flow diagram trace the flow of information in the analysis of control systems.

Third, all control systems are integrated systems of components, in which all the components affect the overall behavior of the system. The relative size of a component is of no consequence, but only the manner in which the component processes the signals that flow through it. As a result, a *systems approach* must be used in analysis and design. This approach, by considering the whole system and its environment as an entity, accommodates all the contributions to the system behavior made by the components and by the interactions of the environment.

Fourth, for reasons of economy, virtually all control systems are *feedback systems* in that signals downstream in the information flow streams are returned upstream of the system to moderate the behavior of the system.

Fifth, and finally, the existence of feedback signal loops, even though all the individual components in the loop are stable, i.e., have no tendency to become deranged when disturbed, introduces the possibility of *instability* in the control loop. The conditions that make for *stability* in the system are a convenient measure of the controllability of the system and a useful basis for control system design.

1-9   System dynamics

Control systems by definition are characterized by organized activity, and as a consequence many properties of the systems change over time. The laws or rules governing these changes constitute the dynamics of the systems.

Dynamic systems are described most usefully by differential equations, with time as the independent variable. Fortunately for control

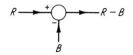

Summer or summation point

Operational block

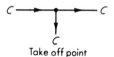

Take off point   *Figure 1-1*   Block-diagram elements.

systems, many situations can be described readily by a narrow class of differential equations.   The appropriate mathematics for these equations and strategies for dealing with less tractable situations are developed in subsequent chapters.

1-10   *Signal-flow diagram*

The basic graphical representation of a control system is the signal-flow diagram.   Indeed, many control problems are solved once the signal-flow diagram can be drawn, since the drawing of the diagram requires a detailed understanding of the system and its dynamics.

Although there are a variety of information-flow representations, we make special use of the block diagram.   In this diagram there are only three types of information-processing elements, as shown in Fig. 1-1.

Note that the summer merely adds the signals entering the circle in accordance with the signs identified at the appropriate entries.   The takeoff point does not alter the incoming signal in any way.

In general, the operational block may be regarded as a *transducer* in that it converts an incoming signal M to an output signal MG.   The conversion comes about by virtue of the operation of G on M.   As will be shown in subsequent chapters, G, the transfer function of the element designated by the block, is an operational representation of the differential equation relating the output signal to the input signal.

1-11   *Simple control system*

An example of a simple control system is the heat-transfer system shown diagrammatically in Fig. 1-2.

The principal process element is a double-pipe heat exchanger in

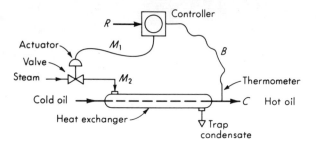

Figure 1-2   Simple heat-transfer system.

which cold oil flowing through the inner pipe is heated by steam condensing in the jacket surrounding the inner pipe.   A control valve, driven by a motor (actuator), manipulates the pressure, and hence the temperature, of the steam in the jacket.   The actuator, in turn, is driven by a controller, which generates a controlling action related to the difference between the measured temperature of the hot oil leaving the exchanger and the desired temperature of the hot oil as set by a reference signal in the controller.

The corresponding block diagram for this heat-exchanger system is shown in Fig. 1-3.   It is the typical diagram of a simple single-loop feedback control system.

The symbols in both figures typically have the following significance:

$$M = \text{manipulated variables}$$
$$B = \text{feedback signals}$$
$$G \text{ and } H = \text{transfer functions, the former in the feedforward part of the loop and the latter in the feedback path}$$

More specifically,

$$R = \text{reference signal to controller, position}$$
$$M_1 = \text{controller output signal, air pressure}$$
$$M_2 = \text{valve output, steam pressure on exchanger jacket}$$

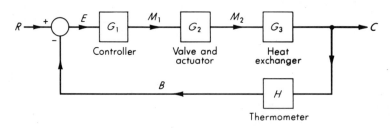

Figure 1-3   Signal-flow diagram for simple feedback control system.

C = controlled variable, actual oil outlet temperature

B = signal from thermometer in hot-oil stream

E = error signal (or deviation), $R - B$

G_1 = transfer function for controller

G_2 = transfer function for final control elements (actuator plus valve)

G_3 = transfer function for heat exchanger

H = transfer function for thermometer

1-12 Systems engineering

A significant feature of Fig. 1-3 is the fact that the four operational blocks are all the same size despite the fact that the heat exchanger might be hundreds of times the size of the thermometer, and the energy fluxes in these two elements might differ by an even larger factor.

From the standpoint of the control system performance, all elements are important, and their simultaneous actions and interactions dictate the behavior of the system. The name *systems engineering* is given to engineering that considers in analysis and design the behavior of the system as a whole, which behavior results from all the actions and interactions of the component elements with each other and with the system's environment.

For the simple system described above, conventional process engineering would produce a design of the heat exchanger which would meet a given specification of steady-state thermal-transport duty. Systems engineering, on the other hand, would lead to a design of the entire heat-exchange system, including valves, controller, and thermometer, which would be based on the dynamic behavior of the integrated system.

In the case of this simple example, it is not likely that systems engineering would produce a significantly better design than would result from the traditional procedure of designing the exchanger first and then hanging on appropriate instrumentation based on successful past experiences. In the case of more complicated systems, however, involving coupled process units and many significant variables, no successful design is possible without taking into account the overall dynamic behavior of the integrated system. Systems engineering for such systems is the only practicable approach to analysis and design.

1-13 Feedback

The control system of Figs. 1-2 and 1-3 is a feedback control system. A downstream signal, namely, the hot-oil temperature, is fed back to the controller and, through comparison with the reference signal R, is used to generate the control-action signal M_1.

The effect of the feedback is to make the controller cognizant of the effects of its action on the variables being controlled.   Thus, in the example of Figs. 1-2 and 1-3, any change in the hot-oil temperature would result in a corrective change in the steam pressure on the jacket.

Without feedback it would be prohibitively expensive to maintain even a modest regulation of the hot-oil temperature because every pertinent input variable, such as cold-oil temperature and flow rate and steam-supply pressure, would have to be monitored, and appropriate actions would have to be generated to offset the anticipated effects of changes in the monitored variables.   Purely feedforward control by itself is not practicable, although, as will be seen, certain feedback control systems can be improved by the addition of feedforward sequences.

1-14   Stability

It is shown in Chap. 6 that controllers are signal amplifiers, among other things.   For feedback systems, the larger the amplification in the controller, the greater in general is the accuracy of control, because the error required to generate a given control action is smaller, and accuracy of control is measured by the smallness of the error, or deviation of the controlled variable from the desired reference value.

Unfortunately, the amplification in the controller in a feedback system cannot be increased without limit.   All real feedback control systems tend to become unstable with increasing amplification in the controller. The evidence of this tendency is the appearance of oscillations in the controlled variable.   In a stable system the oscillations die out in time, but in an unstable system the oscillations grow in magnitude until the system breaks down or some condition of saturation is reached.

The limiting condition in a process control system between stability and instability is characterized by steady cycling of the process variables. This limiting condition of stability can be found readily from the *frequency-response* characteristics of the individual components of the control loop.   These characteristics define the response of the system to sustained cyclic forcing.

Subsequent chapters show how frequency-response characteristics may be obtained for loop elements and overall loops and how these may be used as a basis for control system design.

two

control system
performance

Performance must be gauged in terms of objectives.   In this chapter the objectives of control systems are discussed generally, and also for representative process systems, as a basis for identifying useful criteria of performance quality.   Dynamic responses are introduced as the measure of dynamic performance, and some common characterizations of these responses are described.   The use of frequency response in control system design is discussed briefly in order to present specifications of performance in terms of frequency-response characteristics.

2-1   *Control system objectives*

The performance objectives of process systems are concerned ultimately with economic optimizations.   A chemical plant may be required to produce a particular chemical product at some particular rate and level of quality, but what is actually sought is a maximizing of the overall economic advantage to the owners of the plant.

The continuous automatic optimization of the performance of a process plant, or any other system of comparable complexity, would require the coupling of elaborate automatic computing equipment to the plant.   Elaborate equipment would be required because large amounts of information on a wide variety of economic and process properties would have to be processed to gauge reliably the consequence of all possible courses of action.   Some aspects of the problems involved in incorporating automatic computation in feedback control systems are treated in Chap. 10.

In practice today most process systems are designed to approximate to some kind of optimum performance based on past experience.   Overall capacities and throughputs for the systems usually are set somewhat arbitrarily, depending upon estimates of market potential, availability of raw materials and capital, and similar factors.   The design of the process is worked out so that the desired capacities and product qualities may be achieved within reasonable limits.   The design of the control system which incorporates the process is worked out so that the system is stable and the effects of externally imposed disturbances are small.

Thus, although the ultimate objectives of control systems ideally should be specified in terms of optimizing functions, practical objectives may be specified in terms of system stability and the manner in which the system accommodates disturbances.

2-2   *Types of control systems*

There are two different types of automatic control systems, namely, *servomechanisms* and *regulators*.   The same general signal-flow diagram shown in Fig. 2-1 suffices for both systems, but in servomechanisms the principal forcing variable, or input variable, is the reference signal, also called the set point, or command signal, R, whereas in regulators the principal forcing variable is the disturbance signal U.

For performance analysis the signal-flow diagram for the servomechanism may be abbreviated as shown in Fig. 2-2a, and for the regulator, as shown in Fig. 2-2b.

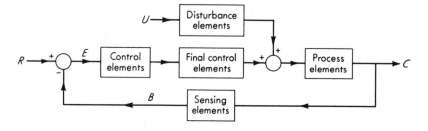

Figure 2-1 Signal-flow diagram for simple control system.

2-3 Servomechanisms

Servomechanisms are subjected to changing command signals, and the control objective is to maintain a close correspondence between the reference and the controlled variable. Typical examples are the many kinds of position control systems used in vessel steering, automatic gun-fire control, missile guidance, and in valve positioners.

2-4 Regulators

Process control systems are usually regulators in that the function of the system is to hold the controlled variables steady at the values set by the reference despite any disturbances imposed externally. Program-controlled batch processes, in which the reference signal undergoes a preset pattern in time, would be regarded as servomechanisms within our definition.

2-5 Local objectives

The objectives for the servomechanism and the regulator may be written, respectively,

$$\frac{C}{R} \to 1.0 \tag{2-1}$$

$$\frac{R - C}{U} \to 0 \tag{2-2}$$

Figure 2-2 Abbreviated signal-flow diagram.

where the former gives the *control ratio* and the latter gives the *deviation ratio* for regulation.

In words, for the servomechanism, changes in the command signal R should be reflected promptly in equal changes in the controlled variable C; and for regulators, the error, or deviation, signal $E = R - C$ should remain small despite the imposition on the system of a disturbance U.

Both objectives may apply to both kinds of systems, since servomechanisms are subjected to outside disturbances, and regulators occasionally may have their set points changed.

2-6   *Feedforward control*

Sometimes control systems are classified in two categories, depending on whether a measure of the controlled variable is used to moderate the controlling action.   Control systems in which this feedback of the controlled variable does not take place are called feedforward control systems.   In the long view, such systems cannot be used alone in process control.   There are many examples of systems which operate for long periods of time as feedforward control systems, but feedback, though intermittent, is always necessary in the long run.   For processes requiring close and economic control, continuous or nearly continuous feedback is essential.

As was mentioned in Sec. 1-13, it is advantageous in some cases to couple feedforward systems to feedback loops.   On this basis we may classify control systems as feedback systems or feedback-plus-feedforward systems.

2-7   *Dynamic response*

Regardless of how we classify control systems, the key to their performance is the manner in which they respond to the various kinds of disturbances or other forcings imposed on them.   Indeed, for all dynamic systems, the basis of analysis is the behavior in time of the principal time-varying properties of the system following some manipulation of the system.   This behavior is the *dynamic response* of the system.   The manipulation that causes the response is an input signal called the *forcing signal,* driving signal, or simply, the *forcing.*

An example of forcing and response in a simple case would be the situation in the heat-exchanger system of Fig. 1-1 when a sudden change occurred in the temperature of the inlet cold oil.   This temperature

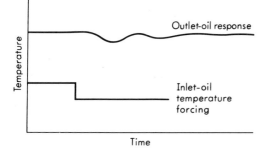

Figure 2-3   Typical dynamic response of a control system.

change would be the forcing signal to the system, and the dynamic response of principal interest would be the temporal behavior of the temperature of the hot oil leaving the exchanger.   A typical response for this kind of feedback control system is shown in Fig. 2-3, together with the forcing signal.

Every dynamic system can be depicted by its response to forcing, but for complicated systems the representation is difficult.   An example of the difficulty would be given by attempting to analyze the dynamic response of a perceptive human being following exposure to a beautiful work of art.   Not the least of the difficulties would be the identification and measurement of the significant responding variables.

Fortunately, most process systems can be reduced to combinations of tractable elements, and the important process variables are easily identified.

For the servomechanism the forcing variable is the reference input, and for the regulator it is the disturbance input.   In both cases, the important response is the true value of the controlled variable.   The forcing and the response are functions of time which are uniquely related to each other by the characteristics of the system.   We use the convention of identifying functions of time by lowercase letters.   Thus the respective forcing functions for servomechanisms and regulators are r and u, and the response function is c.   Uppercase letters, such as those in Figs. 2-1 and 2-2 and in Eqs. (2-1) and (2-2), designate transformed variables, which are defined later.

The analysis problem for dynamic systems is concerned with determining the characteristics of the system from observed responses to particular forcings.   On the other hand, the design problem involves choosing the characteristics of the system in such a manner that economically desirable responses are obtained for normal and typical forcings.

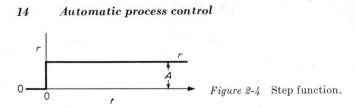

Figure 2-4   Step function.

Although actual forcings may involve a wide variety of functions of time, it is desirable in both design and analysis to make use of a very few standardized forcing functions which are easily manipulated.   Five such functions are described below.

2-8   *Step function*

The step function, or *constant forcing*, is characterized by the fact that, for all prior time, the forcing variable is steady at some value; then it jumps instantaneously to a new value, and for all subsequent time remains steady at the new value.   It is generally convenient to assume that the change occurs at time zero and to assume, further, that the forcing variable is a perturbation about the original steady value.   The effect of both of these assumptions is to set the initial conditions for the forcing event equal to zero.

Figure 2-4 shows step forcing of magnitude A with r as the perturbed forcing variable.   Thus

$$r = \begin{cases} 0 & \text{for } t < 0 \\ A & \text{for } t \geq 0 \end{cases} \tag{2-3}$$

2-9   *Ramp function*

The ramp function, or *constant-rate forcing*, is characterized by the fact that, at time zero and for all time thereafter, the forcing variable changes at a constant rate as shown in Fig. 2-5.   Again it is convenient to regard the forcing variable as a perturbation about an original steady

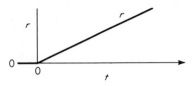

Figure 2-5   Ramp function.

value, and thus

$$r = \begin{cases} 0 & \text{for } t \le 0 \\ kt & \text{for } t > 0 \end{cases} \tag{2-4}$$

where k is the slope of the ramp, and t is the time.

2-10   *Pulse function*

A pulse function occurs when the forcing variable changes from its initial condition at time zero and then at some subsequent time returns to the initial condition. There are many kinds and shapes of pulses. Two that are particularly useful, one from the standpoint of experimental testing, the other from the standpoint of mathematical convenience, are the rectangular pulse, which is formed by two successive steps of equal magnitude but opposite sign, shown in Fig. 2-6, and the *unit impulse*, which is a pulse of unit integral area but zero duration. The unit impulse is treated in some detail in Chap. 4.

Pulses are particularly useful in dealing with operating systems because there is no prolonged derangement of process variables and, further, because pulses are readily imposed on input variables.

2-11   *Steady-state sinusoid*

The fourth and most useful forcing function for dealing with feedback control systems is the steady-state sine wave, given by

$$r = A \sin \omega t \tag{2-5}$$

where A = amplitude of sine wave
ω = angular frequency, rad/time
t = time

This function is shown in Fig. 2-7, plotted to an arbitrary time scale as oscillations about zero. The starting time is of no consequence for this forcing because the relevant response is that which is observed after

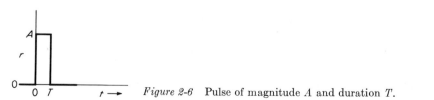

Figure 2-6   Pulse of magnitude A and duration T.

the sinusoidal forcing has been going on long enough for all transient effects to have disappeared.

2-12   *Random forcing*

In operating process systems all variables are continually changing. Although the changes are small and random for well-controlled systems, they are the actual forcings and responses for the operating system, and they can be correlated statistically and used for analyzing the dynamics of elements in the system.   Extensive machine computation is required to reduce and interpret the data, but for operating plants, the use of random forcing in principle offers a means of dynamic analysis which eliminates the need to disturb the process in any way.

A related forcing which combines some of the features of the sinusoidal forcing and random forcing is obtained by applying a low-level periodic signal which is of no greater amplitude than the peaks in the random input signals.   The response to this forcing can be analyzed by filtering out the purely random part of the response, the so-called *noise* in the signal.

2-13   *Useful forcing functions*

There are other forcing functions—for example, constant-acceleration forcing is important in designing servomechanisms—but for process control the foregoing five are the principal ones.   We make particular use of the step function and the steady-state sinusoid, the former because it is a severe but easily visualizable imposition, and the latter because it is the basis of *frequency response.*

2-14   *Transient response*

The dynamic response of a system to any forcing is made up of a steady-state part and a transient part.   For stable systems the transient

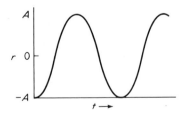

Figure 2-7   Steady-state sinusoid.

part of the response is that part which dies away with increasing time. This transient response provides a convenient and readily recognizable measure of the dynamic performance of a control system.

By way of illustration, let us consider various step responses produced in a simple control system like the heat-exchanger system depicted in Fig. 1-1. If the heat exchanger has been operating steadily with an outlet-oil temperature of 150°F, and the set point of the controller is suddenly increased from 150 to 160°, we might expect the outlet-oil temperature to follow one of the response curves shown in Fig. 2-8.

These curves, marked I, II, and III, are time plots of the controlled variable c immediately following a step change of A in the set point r, which would correspond to the 10° perturbation from 150 to 160°. The curves are for the same control system, but in each succeeding case from I to III, the control sensitivity has been increased by adjusting the controller so that a greater controller output signal results from a given error input signal. We shall not attempt a more precise definition of control sensitivity at this juncture.

Curve I represents an *overdamped case;* curve II is the *critically damped case;* and curve III is an *underdamped case.* Critical damping is the condition where the response is the fastest possible without overshoot, that is, without the response exceeding its final steady-state value.

As the control sensitivity is increased, the response becomes faster, as indicated by more rapid rate of rise, but the system becomes less stable, i.e., less damped, as indicated by tendencies toward oscillation. With further increase in sensitivity, a point is reached where the response is a

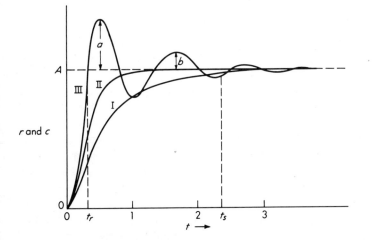

Figure 2-8   Typical step responses.

sustained oscillation at constant amplitude, and any further increase in sensitivity would result in oscillations of increasing amplitude and ultimate runaway, or breakdown, of the system.   Actually, for the heat-exchanger system under consideration, a condition of *saturation* would intervene before a runaway condition could occur.   The controller in the unstable case would become saturated in the sense that its output would swing from zero to full output, corresponding to zero steam and full line-pressure steam on the exchanger jacket, respectively.   As a result, the controlled variable, namely, the temperature of the hot oil, would undergo large and sustained oscillations.

2-15   *Dynamic performance criteria based on step response*

Clearly, the optimum dynamic response of a control system must be a compromise between the sluggishness of overdamping and the instability of excessive sensitivity.

For many process control systems a practical optimum response is one which is slightly underdamped, with an *initial overshoot*, for example, a/A of curve III in Fig. 2-8, not exceeding about 30 percent, and a *subsidence ratio a/b* of about 3:1.   The subsidence ratio is the ratio of the amplitudes of successive cycles in a decaying oscillation.

For some systems less overshoot, or even no oscillation, may be permissible.   In such cases critical damping, or nearly so, may be the best response.

Specifications of the extent of damping do not deal directly with the speed of the response, and hence a further specification may be necessary.   One measure of the speed of response of a system is the settling time t_s on curve III, which is the time it takes for the system following step forcing to settle down to a deviation between command and response less than, say, 5 percent of the final steady value.

A similar measure is the rise time t_r, which is the shortest time required for the response to a step to first come up to some specified percentage, such as 90 percent of the final value of the response.

In the unattainably ideal case, where the economic penalties for all deviations of the controlled variable from the desired reference are known, the specification for dynamic performance would be simply that the cost of maintaining a required operation be minimal.   For real systems an arbitrary approximation to this specification of performance might be that the time integral of the absolute value of the difference between the reference and the controlled response be minimal for a given forcing, or that the time integral of the square of the difference be minimal.

2-16 Direct design from transient response

Regardless of what particular specifications are set for the transient response of a control system, it is not in general possible to undertake a design directly based on these specifications. Such a design would require that the system be described precisely by mathematical equations, which would have to be solved for the particular transient response of interest. Not only is the solution of the equations for systems of typical real complexity quite difficult, but the determination of system modifications which are required to match the specified response generally cannot be done analytically.

A practical design can be approximated by trial and error on analog computing machines, but even relatively simple process systems require a large computer for reasonable simulation. In subsequent chapters we elaborate somewhat on what may be done with large-scale automatic computers, both analog and digital.

2-17 Frequency response

Rather than attempt to solve the direct design problem, we make use of *frequency response* and related techniques. These techniques were developed to a high degree of utility for servomechanisms during World War II, and since then they have been adapted successfully for a wide variety of process control systems.

The frequency response of a system is the response of the system to steady-state sinusoidal forcing over wide ranges of frequency. Consider the system of Fig. 2-9, which is forced by a sustained sinusoidal signal at constant amplitude A and constant frequency ω. Following common practice, we designate process variables in the frequency domain by capital letters, R and C.

If the amplitude of the input signal is small, the response signal for virtually all process elements will be another sine wave having the same frequency but with a different amplitude and a displacement of the output wave with respect to the input wave. In the figure this response is identified as $B \sin (\omega t + \psi)$, where ψ is the angular displacement of the output sine wave from the input wave.

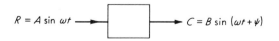

$R = A \sin \omega t \longrightarrow \boxed{} \longrightarrow C = B \sin (\omega t + \psi)$

Figure 2-9 Sinusoidally forced element.

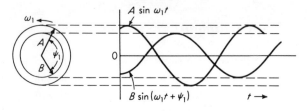

Figure 2-10   Sinusoids as rotating vectors.

The frequency response has particular significance for *linear systems*. A precise definition of linear systems is that they are systems describable by linear differential equations, and we elaborate this definition in Chap. 3.   For the present purposes it will suffice to define a linear system as one for which the total response to a forcing which consists of a summation of a number of individual forcings is exactly equal to the sum of all the individual responses to those forcings.   This definition is a statement of the *principle of superposition.*

The frequency-response characteristics of a linear system are given at each frequency by the ratio of the amplitude of the response sinusoid to the amplitude of the forcing sinusoid, B/A, and by the phase shift between the two sinusoids, ψ.   A simple representation of these quantities at a single frequency is shown in Fig. 2-10, where the sine waves are regarded as being generated by the ordinate projections of a pair of vectors rotating counterclockwise at steady angular velocity ω_1, having lengths A and B equal to the amplitudes of the forcing and response vectors, respectively, and displaced from each other by an angle ψ_1.   In this representation the phase angle ψ_1 is a negative number since the response vector lags behind the forcing vector by ψ_1 rad.

Thus the frequency-response characteristics are

$$\text{Amplitude ratio or magnitude ratio} = \left| \frac{C}{R} \right| = \frac{B}{A} \qquad (2\text{-}6)$$

$$\text{Phase angle} = \underline{/\frac{C}{R}} = \psi \qquad (2\text{-}7)$$

As shown in Chap. 3, the frequency-response characteristics may be computed readily if the dynamic equations for the system are known; for existing systems they may be determined directly by measurement; and for simple systems they may be estimated from step or other dynamic responses.

For most process systems at increased frequencies the magnitude ratio falls off and the *phase lag*, defined as the negative of the phase angle, increases. That is to say, the system at high frequencies is incapable of following the forcing.

Example 2-1 A frequency-response test was made on the heat exchanger of Fig. 1-1 by causing steam pressure on the exchanger to oscillate steadily between 15 and 18 psig at a period of 10 min. The temperature of the heated fluid leaving the exchanger oscillated between 129 and 151°F, but the peak temperature was not reached until 3 min after the peak in steam pressure. The steady-state temperatures of the outlet oil corresponding to the two steam pressures were found to be 122 and 158°F. Calculate the frequency-response characteristics.

Solution Instead of using the ratio of fluid temperature to steam pressure, we compute a dimensionless magnitude ratio by using the idea of the *potential value*. This value is merely the steady-state equivalent of one variable in terms of another, sometimes referred to as the *steady-state gain*. The potential value of the steam oscillation is an amplitude of $(158 - 122)/2$, or 18°F, and therefore the magnitude ratio of response to forcing is $(151 - 129)/18$, or 0.61.

The phase angle is $-(3)(360)/10$, or $-108°$, and the frequency is $2\pi/10$, or 0.628 rad/min, or $\frac{1}{10}$ cycle/min.

2-18 *Frequency-response graphics*

Frequency-response characteristics may be expressed graphically in many ways. On the *Nyquist diagram*, or *polar frequency-response diagram*, the vector locus of system response to unit amplitude forcing is plotted in polar form for all frequencies. The inverse *Nyquist diagram*, or *inverse polar frequency-response* diagram, is the same kind of plot for the reciprocal function, namely, the forcing required for unit response. In the *gain-phase*, or *magnitude-phase*, plot the logarithm of the magnitude ratio of response to forcing is plotted against phase angle.

In later chapters these diagrams are shown to have particular usefulness in different types of applications.

2-19 *Bode diagram*

All three plots have the disadvantage that frequencies are not readily identifiable, since each point on a curve corresponds to a particular frequency. This disadvantage is overcome, and some additional advantages are achieved, by the *Bode diagram*, in which separate curves are plotted for the logarithm of the magnitude ratio and for the phase angle, both as functions of the logarithm of the frequency.

In serial arrays of dynamic elements in a control system, the overall magnitude ratio of the array at a given frequency is obtained by multiplying together the individual magnitude ratios of the elements, and the overall phase angle is obtained by summing the individual angles.   Both of these operations may be accomplished on a Bode diagram by graphical summation.   Furthermore, the nature of the coordinates makes it possible to use straight-line approximations for the characteristics of many common types of process elements.

A typical Bode diagram for a process system is shown in Fig. 2-11. Note that the magnitude ratio falls off and the phase angle becomes increasingly lagging with increasing frequency.

Among some control engineers it is the practice to plot both magnitude ratio and phase angle on the same graph by expressing the magnitude ratio in decibels, given by the defining relation

$$L = 20 \log \text{MR} \tag{2-8}$$

where L is the log modulus in decibels (db), and MR is the magnitude ratio.

This device permits the use of semilog graph paper to plot both

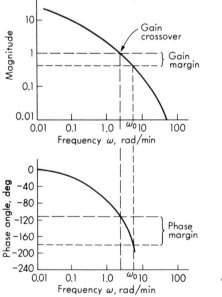

Figure 2-11   Typical open-loop Bode diagram.

magnitude ratio and phase as ordinate on the linear scale versus frequency on the logarithmic scale as shown in Fig. 2-12.

2-20 Limiting condition of stability and frequency response

In Sec. 2-14 we intimated that the limiting condition between stability and instability in a control system occurs when the control sensitivity is increased sufficiently to produce a sustained cycling in the system response. Since frequency response is concerned specifically with sustained cycling, we can use frequency-response characterization to identify the limiting condition of stability.

Instability, or the limiting condition between stability and instability, will result when signals are propagated around the control loop without decay, i.e., without a decrease in amplitude with each passage around the loop. Since the effect of the process elements and the sensing elements usually will be to attenuate or diminish signals, it will be necessary for instability for the controller elements and the final control elements to exert a counterbalancing amplification of signals.

On the Bode diagram the amplification in the controller required for instability can be identified by plotting the overall open-loop frequency-response characteristics, using the deviation input to the controller elements as the forcing signal and the response of the sensing elements as the final open-loop response. A block diagram of this open-loop system is shown in Fig. 2-13. Note that the feedback signal B has been disconnected from the summer, with the result that the set point is equal to the deviation input.

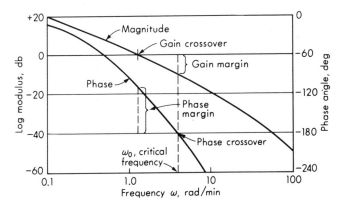

Figure 2-12 Typical open-loop Bode diagram with magnitude in decibels.

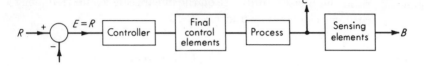

Figure 2-13   Simple control system with the loop open.

2-21   *Critical frequency*

Since the effect of the summing point located between the reference input and the deviation input is to change the sign of the response, or feedback signal, B, the result of closing the loop through the summing point is to add an additional lag angle of 180° to the open-loop phase. Therefore the critical frequency for the system is the frequency at which the open-loop phase is $-180°$, since this is the frequency for which the total angle, including the summer, is $-360°$, and hence it is the frequency at which signals going around the closed loop are in phase on each succeeding circuit of the loop.   If the overall open-loop magnitude ratio for this frequency is made equal to unity (0 db), the system will be at the limiting condition of stability.

We may visualize this condition in Fig. 2-13 as follows:

First we subject the reference R to a sustained sinusoidal forcing perturbation at unit amplitude and at the critical frequency ω_0.   If the controller has been adjusted to provide sufficient magnification of signal at this frequency to offset exactly the diminution of signal that occurs in the rest of the loop, the feedback signal B will be a sinusoidal perturbation of unit amplitude and frequency ω_0, but it will be exactly 180° out of phase with the error signal.

Now, if we simultaneously close the loop by connecting the feedback line to the summing point and discontinue the perturbation of the reference input, there will continue to be sinusoidal perturbations flowing around the loop.   The feedback signals with their signs reversed by the summer produce precisely the same signal in E as when the loop was open, and therefore the sinusoidal signals flow around the closed loop at constant frequency, and at any point the amplitude is constant in time.

2-22   *Design via frequency response*

Once the conditions which make for instability in a control system have been identified, the design problem is reduced to the relatively simple problem of relaxing these conditions to a stable condition based on experience. The possible directions of the relaxation are determined by the nature of the design problem.

In a typical case the process elements are known but not accessible to appreciable alteration in characteristics. The design problem, then, is principally one of specifying what kinds of controllers and final control elements are required for given specifications of control system performance.

Contemporary Russian literature on automatic control divides the design problem, and the analysis problem as well, into the *stability problem* and the *quality problem*. One important aspect of control quality is the relative stability of the system, and we may specify a practical degree of stability in terms of frequency-response characteristics, using a few empirical rules.

Experience has shown that a good stable control system will result in most commonly encountered cases if the overall open-loop magnitude ratio is set equal to 0.4 to 0.5 (−8.0 to −6.0 db) at the critical frequency. This rule is stated alternatively by saying that the *gain margin* at phase crossover should be 2.5 to 2.0 (8.0 to 6.0 db). *Gain margin* is the factor by which the overall magnitude ratio is safely removed from, i.e., less than, 1.0 (0 db). *Phase crossover* is the frequency at which the overall open-loop phase angle first reaches the critical condition of −180°.

A companion rule is that the phase margin should lie between 45 and 60° at gain crossover. *Phase margin* is the number of degrees by which the overall open-loop phase angle is safely removed from, i.e., is numerically smaller than, the critical angle of −180°. *Gain crossover* is the frequency at which the overall open-loop magnitude ratio is unity (0 db).

The application of these rules in general produces slightly underdamped control systems, which typically respond to step forcings with 20 to 30 percent overshoots followed by decays at subsidence ratios of about 3:1.

Figures 2-11 and 2-12 illustrate the quantities used in these frequency-response rules in typical Bode diagrams.

Example 2-2 The open-loop frequency-response characteristics of a simple single-loop control system, including the controller but excluding the summer, are found to be as follows:

Frequency, cycles/min	0.01	0.06	0.10	0.06	1.0
Magnitude ratio	4.82	1.00	0.47	0.08	0.02
Phase angle	−10°	−122°	−180°	−272°	−317°

What are the critical frequency, gain margin, and phase margin for this system?

Solution   From the data in the table, the critical frequency is 0.10 cycle/min, which is the frequency at which the overall open-loop phase angle is −180°; the gain margin, which is the safety factor in the magnitude ratio at the critical frequency, is 1.00/0.47, or 2.13; and the phase margin, which is the margin of safety in the phase angle at gain crossover (overall magnitude equal to unity), is 180 − 122, or 58°.

2-23   Steady-state error

The design of control systems using the frequency-response rules for gain margin and phase margin results in systems which are stable and which in general have satisfactory transient response.   These rules do not bear very directly on accuracy of control.   As is shown in subsequent chapters, many control systems will tolerate steady-state error.   To eliminate such error, a separate analysis must be made by focusing attention on the frequency-response characteristics at the steady state, namely, at zero frequency.

The treatment of steady-state error is considered in Chap. 6 and in detail in Chap. 9.

2-24   Speed of response

The frequency-response rules for reasonable stability do not provide any kind of specification of the desirable speeds of response of the control system.   Clearly, the speed of response must be related to the critical frequency of the system, but no general specification can be made beyond the statement that the speed generally should be rapid rather than slow. Again, Chaps. 6 and 9 treat this aspect of system performance in some detail.

2-25   Overall system performance

In the preceding sections we have outlined very briefly the steps involved in undertaking the simplest kind of design of a control system using frequency-response characterization.   First the limiting condition of stability was found, and then empirical rules were invoked to back off from this condition to a practical condition of stability.

We have chosen to introduce some simple elements of design here as a prelude to succeeding chapters.   In order to apply the frequency-response rules for design we must know the practical extents to which the characteristics of elements in the control system can be altered.

We can gauge the overall performance of automatic process control systems only if we can first gauge the performance of the various elements which make up the total system.   The next four chapters take up the dynamic characteristics of the elements shown in Fig. 2-1 in sequential order around the loop, beginning with the process itself.

three

process dynamics

Dynamic systems are time-varying systems, and descriptions of their behavior make use of differential equations with time as the independent variable. Since process control systems are usually regulators with fixed set points, the dynamic behavior consists largely of modest excursions of the various process variables about steady operating points. This kind of behavior can be described quite accurately by linear differential equations, and for these equations the techniques of operational calculus can be used to simplify greatly the mathematical notation and manipulation.

In this chapter the important process elements are classified into a few basic categories, depending on the form of the mathematical equation describing their dynamics. Typical responses to various kinds of forcing are examined in detail for representative lumped-parameter elements, i.e., elements describable by ordinary, as opposed to partial, differential equations.

3-1   Simple and complex elements

We may divide dynamic elements into two broad classes: simple elements comprising systems which may be described by ordinary linear differential equations with constant coefficients and order not greater than second, and complex elements comprising all other elements.

3-2   First-order transfer stage

The simplest of simple elements is the *first-order transfer stage*, sometimes also called *first-order element, first-order lag*, or *first-order RC stage*. Its dynamics are completely described by an equation of the form

$$T \frac{dy}{dt} + y = x(t) \tag{3-1}$$

where T = time constant of stage
y = output signal, or response
x = input, or forcing, signal, a function of time
t = time

This equation is *linear* in that the dependent variable y and its derivative appear in terms which are first-degree, i.e., raised to the first power only. It is an *ordinary differential equation* since there are no partial derivatives; and it is *first-order* because the first derivative is the highest order of that derivative of the dependent variable with respect to the independent variable appearing in the equation. The specification of constant coefficients is an additional restriction beyond the specification of linearity, since equations with coefficients which are functions of time only are also linear if the dependent-variable terms are all first-degree. A single constant characterizes the first-order equation, and it is customary to make it the coefficient of the derivative term so that it has the dimensions of time.

Many systems may be described quite reliably by Eq. (3-1). Among them are simple thermometers, liquid-storage tanks, and continuous stirred-tank reactors such as, for example, fluidized-bed catalytic crackers considered as thermal systems.

3-3   Linearity

Although the definition of a linear differential equation given in the preceding section is an adequate one, which by implication serves to define what is meant by a linear element or system, the practical importance of linearity warrants some elaboration.

Linear systems are systems for which the principle of superposition is valid. This principle states that the response of a system subjected to a number of forcings simultaneously or at different times, at the same point or at different points, is given by adding up the individual responses computed for each forcing taken alone.

One important aspect of this principle, and hence one test for linearity, is the fact that the frequency-response characteristics of linear systems are independent of the amplitude of the forcing sine wave.

For nonlinear systems, that is, systems which cannot be described by linear differential equations, the principle of superposition does not apply and frequency-response characteristics no longer have any general significance. Since there are no general mathematics for treating nonlinear differential equations, no general analysis is possible. As described in Chap. 10, some limited techniques are available for dealing with certain special cases, and large-scale computing machines, both analog and digital, can handle nonlinear problems, but not always economically.

3-4   Perturbations about normal operating levels

Before we consider some typical first-order process systems, it is convenient at this time to introduce the concept of small perturbations to simplify our mathematical treatment.

Process control systems operate normally with the various process variables holding fairly steady at the normal and constant operating levels. The process variables will be subject to modest excursions about these levels, but if the system is well designed, the excursions will be quite small.

In a typical continuous chemical reactor producing an effluent gas stream containing 1.3 percent product and 98.7 percent inert materials, the percent product might jump erratically from 1.28 percent to 1.31 percent and result in apparent fluctuations on the recording chart in the range 1.29 to 1.30 percent.   In a typical household heating system the observable changes in thermometer reading will be less than 0.5°F at 72°F.

These perturbations of the variables from their normal operating levels are so small, being less than one or two percent of the operating levels, that the capacity coefficients, rate coefficients, and other properties of the fluids and apparatus are essentially constant, and consequently, as shown in Sec. 3-10, the dynamic behavior of the system can be described reliably by linear differential equations, even though the basic process equations are inherently nonlinear.

For most problems in process dynamics it will be advantageous to write the dynamical equations in terms of the perturbations rather than the absolute values of the variables.   The particular convenience of this strategy will be more apparent with the use of operational calculus, but we make immediate use of the strategy to avoid ambiguities in nomenclature.

We may regard the absolute value of a process variable as being the sum of a normal operating value and a small perturbation from that operating value.   If we let the subscript s denote the normal operating values, the absolute values of a variable are given by $x_s + x$, where x is the perturbation.

We may rewrite Eq. (3-1) in terms of this sum as follows:

$$T \frac{d(y_s + y)}{dt} + y_s + y = x_s + x \qquad (3\text{-}2)$$

When the system described by this equation is in steady operation at normal operating conditions, the perturbations are zero.   Since dy_s/dt is also zero by definition, $y_s = x_s$, and consequently

$$T \frac{dy}{dt} + y = x \qquad (3\text{-}3)$$

where now all the y and x are perturbations.   This equation is the same as Eq. (3-1), indicating that we may write the same equation for absolute values or for perturbations.   Usually, it will be advantageous to use the idea of perturbation for equations in which time is the independent variable.

3-5   Simple thermal system

A familiar example of a first-order transfer stage is the thermometric system in Fig. 3-1, consisting of a well-stirred liquid bath in which is immersed the hot junction of a thermocouple encased in a small silver sphere. The corresponding signal-flow diagram is shown in the same figure.

If we assume that the temperature of the bath is everywhere x, and the temperature of the silver sphere is uniform from the couple junction out to the surface of the sphere at y, we may combine the concepts of conservation and rate process and equate the rate of accumulation of energy in the sphere to the rate at which energy is transferred to the sphere from the bath. Thus

$$mC_p \frac{dy}{dt} = hA(x - y) \tag{3-4}$$

where m = mass of sphere
C_p = heat capacity of sphere at constant pressure
h = surface coefficient of thermal transfer at surface of sphere
A = area of surface of sphere
We may designate the term mC_p as C, the thermal *capacitance* of the sphere, and the term hA as $1/R$, the reciprocal of the resistance to heat flow between the bath and the sphere. Inserting these quantities in Eq. (3-2) and rearranging it gives

$$RC \frac{dy}{dt} + y = x \tag{3-5}$$

This form of equation is the basis for calling simple first-order transfer stages RC stages. The product RC is the time constant of the system T.

3-6 *Continuous stirred-tank reactor as mixer*

Another example of the first-order transfer stage is the continuous stirred-tank reactor (CSTR), in which mixing operations occur or in which simple first-order chemical reactions take place. Figure 3-2 shows such a reactor performing as a perfect mixer.

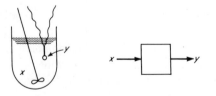

Figure 3-1 Thermocouple in bath.

In this system the volumetric inflow and outflow rates are equal to q, and the respective stream compositions are x and y, expressed in moles of solute per unit volume. A material balance on the solute in the form

Accumulation = inflow − outflow

is

$$V \frac{dy}{dt} = qx - qy \tag{3-6}$$

where V is the volume of liquid in the reactor. Note that perfect mixing is assumed to take place, since the efflux concentration is taken to be the same as the average concentration in the tank. The equation is identically the same as Eq. (3-1) if we divide through by q and set V/q equal to T. For this system the time constant is the *average holdup time* in the reactor, namely, the time required for a volume equal to the liquid volume in the reactor to flow through the reactor.

3-7 CSTR with first-order reaction

Consider the continuous stirred-tank reactor in Fig. 3-2 in which now the chemical reaction

$$A \rightarrow B \tag{3-7}$$

takes place at a rate of ky moles B formed (or moles A consumed) per unit time and per unit volume, where k is the rate coefficient for the reaction, and y is the average concentration of A in the reactor and in the efflux. The differential equation for the concentration of A is given by a material balance on A, allowing for the depletion due to chemical reaction. Thus

$$qx = V \frac{dy}{dt} + kVy + qy \tag{3-8}$$

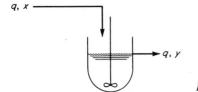

Figure 3-2 Continuous stirred-tank reactor.

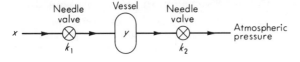

Figure 3-3   Simple pneumatic system.

where all concentration terms are in moles A per unit volume.   Dividing through by q and collecting terms gives

$$T \frac{dy}{dt} + (kT + 1)y = x \tag{3-9}$$

where again T is the average holdup time V/q and the product kT is dimensionless.   The time constant for this system is $T/(kT + 1)$.

3-8   *Air chamber and restriction*

Another example of a system which behaves like a first-order transfer stage is the pneumatic system shown in Fig. 3-3.

Air at a gauge pressure x flows through a restriction, such as a throttled needle valve, into a large volume where the gauge pressure is y, and thence through another restriction to the atmosphere (zero gauge pressure).   If the relative excursions in these pressures are small so that changes in air density are negligible, the material balance for the system may be written

$$C \frac{dy}{dt} = k_1(x - y)^{1/2} - k_2 y^{1/2} \tag{3-10}$$

where C is the capacitance of the air chamber, and the k are the flow coefficients for the restrictions, assuming their behavior approximates that of an orifice in a pipe.   The three terms in the equation are, respectively, the accumulation of air in the vessel, the flow of air into the vessel, and the flow out, all expressed in mass per unit time.

3-9   *Pneumatic capacitance*

The k's in Eq. (3-10) are modified orifice coefficients, and the capacitance C must have the dimensions of mass per unit time divided by change in pressure per unit time, or simply, mass per unit change in pressure.

It is the change in mass of air in the vessel required to produce a unit change in vessel pressure.

For a perfect gas,

$$pV = \frac{m}{\text{MW}} RT \qquad (3\text{-}11)$$

where p = absolute pressure
V = total volume
m = mass of gas in volume V
MW = molecular weight of gas
R = universal gas constant
T = absolute temperature

By definition, the capacitance is

$$C = \frac{dm}{dp}$$

which, by differentiating Eq. (3-11) at constant V, R, T, and MW, is

$$C = \frac{V(\text{MW})}{RT} \qquad (3\text{-}12)$$

Example 3-1 Estimate the pneumatic capacitance of an instrument air-storage tank with a volume of 3.7 ft^3 for air at 30 psig. Express the results using pounds mass for amounts of air and psig (pounds force per square inch gauge) for pressure.

Solution If we assume that the air is at room temperature, say, 70°F, that it has an average molecular weight of 29, and that it behaves ideally at this pressure, Eq. (3-12) applies and

$$C = \frac{(3.7)(29.0)}{(10.73)(460.70)} = 0.019 \text{ lb mass}/(\text{lb force})(\text{in.}^2)$$

3-10 Linearization

In order to make the description of the pneumatic system in Fig. 3-3 tractable, we must linearize the nonlinear terms on the right-hand side of Eq. (3-10). A simple and practical method for this linearization is to expand the nonlinear terms by means of a Taylor series, retaining only linear terms, on the reasonable assumption that only modest excursions occur in the process variables.

Expanding the right-hand terms of Eq. (3-10) for small perturbances Δx and Δy gives, for the first term,

$$k_1(x - y)^{\frac{1}{2}} = k_1(x_s - y_s)^{\frac{1}{2}} + \frac{\partial}{\partial x}[k_1(x - y)^{\frac{1}{2}}]\,\Delta x$$

$$+ \frac{\partial}{\partial y}[k_1(x - y)^{\frac{1}{2}}]\,\Delta y \quad (3\text{-}13)$$

where the partial derivatives, obtained by differentiating the term with respect to one variable while holding all other variables constant, are

$$\frac{\partial[k_1(x - y)^{\frac{1}{2}}]}{\partial x} = \frac{k_1}{2}(x - y)^{-\frac{1}{2}} = a \qquad\qquad (3\text{-}14)$$

and

$$\frac{\partial[k_1(x - y)^{\frac{1}{2}}]}{\partial y} = -\frac{k_1}{2}(x - y)^{-\frac{1}{2}} = -a \qquad\qquad (3\text{-}15)$$

Similarly the expansion of the last term in Eq. (3-10) gives

$$k_2 y^{\frac{1}{2}} = k_2 y_s^{\frac{1}{2}} + \frac{\partial(k_2 y^{\frac{1}{2}})}{\partial y}\,\Delta y \qquad\qquad (3\text{-}16)$$

where

$$\frac{\partial(k_2 y^{\frac{1}{2}})}{\partial y} = \frac{k_2}{2y^{\frac{1}{2}}} = b \qquad\qquad (3\text{-}17)$$

The subscript s in the foregoing equations refers to the steady state as before, and from Eq. (3-10) we see that the steady-state condition is given by

$$0 = k_1(x_s - y_s)^{\frac{1}{2}} - k_2 y_s^{\frac{1}{2}} \qquad\qquad (3\text{-}18)$$

Since $C\,dy/dt = C\,d(\Delta y)/dt$, we may combine Eqs. (3-10) and (3-13) to (3-17) and subtract Eq. (3-18) to get a linearized equation for perturbations in x and y about the steady operating points, namely,

$$C\frac{d(\Delta y)}{dt} = a\,\Delta x - a\,\Delta y - b\,\Delta y$$

or, after dropping the deltas and combining terms,

$$\frac{C}{a}\frac{dy}{dt} + \frac{a+b}{a}y = x \tag{3-19}$$

where now the x and y are perturbations and the constants a, b, and C must be evaluated at the steady operating points. Thus

$$a = \frac{k_1}{2}(x_s - y_s)^{-\frac{1}{2}} \tag{3-20}$$

and

$$b = \frac{k_2}{2y_s^{\frac{1}{2}}} \tag{3-21}$$

The time constant for this system is $C/(a+b)$.

3-11 *First-order-system response to constant forcing*

If the forcing function for a first-order stage is a step of magnitude A, $x(t) = A$, and Eq. (3-1) becomes

$$T\frac{dy}{dt} + y = A \tag{3-22}$$

This kind of forcing could be applied to a simple thermometer-bath system, for example, by abruptly changing the bath temperature from its initial steady condition to some new steady temperature A units greater than the initial condition. In practical cases considerable care is required to introduce a pure step. Often the actual step will be observably rounded at the corners, but fortunately, the effect on the response will be negligible.

We may solve this step-response equation in a variety of ways. The simplest way is to separate the variables y and t and integrate both sides of the equation. Another way is to use operational calculus.

For this problem we use a third method, namely, the classical method for solving differential equations, wherein some form of solution is assumed and then tested in finding the integration constants.

First we assume that the solution consists of the sum of two parts, a *steady-state part*, or particular solution, y_s, and a *transient part*, or complementary solution, y_t, namely,

$$y = y_s + y_t \tag{3-23}$$

Inserting this equation in Eq. (3-22) gives

$$T \frac{d(y_s + y_t)}{dt} + y_s + y_t = A \tag{3-24}$$

Since the steady-state solution, also called the *forced response*, is that which remains after all the transient effects have vanished, it follows from Eq. (3-24) that

$$y_s = A \tag{3-25}$$

and subtracting this result from Eq. (3-24), noting that dy_s/dt is zero, gives

$$T \frac{dy_t}{dt} + y_t = 0 \tag{3-26}$$

Thus we see that the transient part of the solution depends on the characteristics of the system rather than on the nature of the forcing. The total solution, of course, depends on both the forcing and the system characteristics.

The equation for the transient part of the response is *homogeneous* in that all the terms in it involve the dependent variable y_t and its derivatives. We may assume that its solution is of the form

$$y_t = Be^{st} \tag{3-27}$$

and test the validity of our assumption by finding values of the coefficients B and s which satisfy Eqs. (3-23) and (3-26). If we insert Eq. (3-27) into Eq. (3-26) and carry out the indicated differentiation, we find that

$$TsBe^{st} + Be^{st} = 0$$

or

$$(Ts + 1)Be^{st} = 0$$

and therefore, since $Be^{st} \neq 0$,

$$Ts + 1 = 0 \tag{3-28}$$

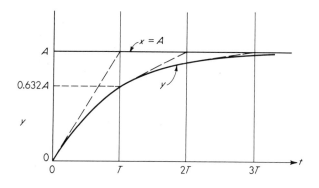

Figure 3-4   First-order step response.

This algebraic equation in s is called the *auxiliary equation*, or *characteristic equation*, of the homogeneous differential equation (3-26).   The roots of the auxiliary equation, i.e., the values of s which satisfy the equation, govern the transient behavior of linear dynamic systems.   In this case the root is a single real negative number, $s = -1/T$.

Now we substitute this value of s in Eq. (3-27) and with Eq. (3-25) rewrite Eq. (3-23) to get

$$y = Be^{-t/T} + A \qquad\qquad (3\text{-}29)$$

But at $t = 0$, $y = 0$ if the y are perturbations, and hence $B = -A$ and Eq. (3-29) becomes

$$y = A(1 - e^{-t/T}) \qquad\qquad (3\text{-}30)$$

This response and the forcing that produced it are shown in Fig. 3-4.

The important properties and the manner of sketching this response are shown in the figure.   For each time interval equal to the time constant T, the recovery that occurs, expressed as a fraction of the forcing at the start of the interval, is $1 - e^{-1} = 0.632$.   Stated another way, the response in any time interval T, after the step, covers 63.2 percent of the amount left to be covered at the start of the time interval.

Furthermore, by differentiating Eq. (3-30) with respect to time and evaluating the derivative at $t = 0$, we find that the slope of the response curve at the start of each interval T is the ratio of the unrecovered part of the step to the time constant T.   At $t = 0$ this ratio is A/T, and at $t = T$ it is $0.368A/T$.

3-12   *Parametric forcing*

A word of caution is in order at this point. The kind of forcing we have described above is not the same as would obtain if we suddenly withdrew a thermometer sensor, such as a thermocouple junction, from a cold agitated bath of water and plunged it into a beaker full of hot water. The forcing, to be sure, would be stepwise, but two different quantities would be step-forced simultaneously, one the driving temperature $x(t)$ and the other the time constant T.

Since the surface coefficient for heat transfer at the surface of the thermometer is different for the thermometer in a cold agitated bath than for the same thermometer in a hot quiescent bath, the time constant T, which is the ratio of thermometer capacitance to surface coefficient, must also be different. This kind of forcing is called *parametric forcing*, because the forcing quantity is a system parameter; that is, it is one of the properties of the system which normally is constant.

For this particular case, the response can be computed simply by using the value of the time constant corresponding to the new conditions.

For systems in which the principal forcing variable is a system parameter, as, for example, in a thermometric system where the flow rate of fluid passing across the sensing bulb of the thermometer is the forcing variable, it is necessary to separate the forcing variable from the response variable in the dynamic equation for the system.

A simple procedure is to expand the dynamic equation in a Taylor series much as was done in Sec. 3-10.

3-13   *Frequency response of first-order systems*

For the sinusoidal forcing of a first-order transfer stage, Eq. (3-1) becomes

$$T \frac{dy}{dt} + y = A \sin \omega t \tag{3-31}$$

where A is the amplitude of the forcing sine wave, and ω is its angular frequency. Again we may assume that the total solution is given by Eq. (3-23), and from insertion in Eq. (3-31), we find that

$$T \frac{dy_t}{dt} + y_t + T \frac{dy_s}{dt} + y_s = A \sin \omega t \tag{3-32}$$

The sum of the first two terms, according to Eq. (3-26), is zero. Indeed, from Eq. (3-27), the transient part of the response must involve a decay term $e^{-t/T}$, but for frequency-response characterization we are interested only in the steady-state response, which, from Eq. (3-32), is

$$T \frac{dy_s}{dt} + y_s = A \sin \omega t \tag{3-33}$$

In this case, however, the steady-state derivative is not zero, since the response must be periodic. As was pointed out in Chap. 2, the response of a linear system to steady-state sinusoidal forcing is observed to be a sinusoid at the same frequency, but usually with a smaller amplitude and displaced from the forcing wave by an angle ψ. Therefore we assume that

$$y_s = B \sin (\omega t + \psi) \tag{3-34}$$

By inserting this equation in Eq. (3-33) and carrying out the indicated differentiation, we obtain

$$B\omega T \cos (\omega t + \psi) + B \sin (\omega t + \psi) = A \sin \omega t \tag{3-35}$$

At $t = 0$, then,

$$B\omega T \cos \psi + B \sin \psi = 0$$

or

$$\frac{\sin \psi}{\cos \psi} = \tan \psi = -\omega T$$

and hence

$$\psi = \tan^{-1} (-\omega T) = \arctan (-\omega T) \tag{3-36}$$

Now, from the trigonometric identities among sums of angles,

$$\cos (\omega T + \psi) = \cos \omega T \cos \psi - \sin \omega T \sin \psi \tag{3-37}$$

and

$$\sin (\omega T + \psi) = \sin \omega T \cos \psi + \cos \omega T \sin \psi \tag{3-38}$$

Furthermore, from the properties of right triangles and the fact of Eq. (3-36), we know that

$$\sin \psi = - \frac{\omega T}{(1 + \omega^2 T^2)^{1/2}} \tag{3-39}$$

and

$$\cos \psi = \frac{1}{(1 + \omega^2 T^2)^{1/2}} \tag{3-40}$$

If we insert these values into Eqs. (3-37) and (3-38) and the resulting expressions into Eq. (3-35) for $t = T$, we find that

$$\frac{B}{A} = \frac{1}{(1 + \omega^2 T^2)^{1/2}} = \cos \psi \tag{3-41}$$

Thus

$$y_s = A(1 + \omega^2 T^2)^{-1/2} \sin (\omega t + \psi)$$
$$= A \cos \psi \sin (\omega t + \psi) \tag{3-42}$$

and the frequency-response characteristics are the phase angle ψ, which is $\tan^{-1}(-\omega T)$, and the magnitude ratio given by Eq. (3-41) is $\cos \psi$, or $1/(1 + \omega^2 T^2)^{1/2}$.

3-14   Nyquist diagram

The locus of all possible values of B/A, plotted on a polar diagram as in Fig. 3-5 for a first-order transfer stage, is a semicircle in the fourth quadrant. At zero frequency the magnitude ratio is 1.0 and the phase angle is zero, which is to say that the incoming and outgoing signals are identical when the system is in the steady unforced state. At infinite

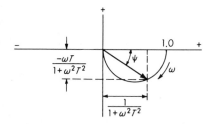

Figure 3-5 Nyquist diagram for first-order transfer stage.

frequency the response signal is fully attenuated, i.e., zero, and the phase angle is $\tan^{-1}(-\infty)$, which is $-\pi/2$ rad, or $-90°$.

This polar diagram, often called a *Nyquist diagram*, may be regarded as the vector locus of the ratio of response to forcing. The vector of unit magnitude along the positive real axis is the forcing-signal magnitude, and a point on the locus identifies the response vector (for unit forcing) at a particular frequency. The angle between the vectors is the phase angle at that frequency. If these vectors are allowed to rotate counter-clockwise at constant frequency while maintaining the angle between them fixed at the angle corresponding to the particular frequency of rotation, the ordinates of the tips of the vectors will trace sine waves as shown in Fig. 2-10.

3-15   *Complex-variable representation of sine waves*

A more convenient manner of handling sinusoidal quantities, which avoids somewhat the need of using trigonometric functions, is based on Euler's equation,

$$\cos \omega t \pm j \sin \omega t = e^{\pm j\omega t} \tag{3-43}$$

and the use of an operator, Im, which has the property of taking only the imaginary part of a complex variable.

Euler's equation may be derived readily by expanding $\cos \omega t$ and $\sin \omega t$ in infinite series in ωt; inserting $j = \sqrt{-1}$ into the ωt terms of both series; and adding the series together after multiplying the sine series by j. Thus, by Maclaurin expansion,

$$\cos \omega t = 1 - \frac{(\omega t)^2}{2!} + \frac{(\omega t)^4}{4!} - \cdots$$

$$= 1 + \frac{(j\omega t)^2}{2!} + \frac{(j\omega t)^4}{4!} + \cdots$$

and similarly,

$$\sin \omega t = \omega t - \frac{(\omega t)^3}{3!} + \frac{(\omega t)^5}{5!} - \cdots$$

$$= \omega t + \frac{j^2(\omega t)^3}{3!} + \frac{j^4(\omega t)^5}{5!} + \cdots$$

Hence

$$\cos \omega t + j \sin \omega t = 1 + j\omega t + \frac{(j\omega t)^2}{2!} + \frac{(j\omega t)^3}{3!} + \cdots$$

which is Eq. (3-43), since the right-hand side is identically $e^{j\omega t}$.

The resulting sum of a real quantity and an imaginary quantity appearing in the left-hand side of Eq. (3-43) is called a *complex quantity*, not because it is complicated, but because it contains both real and imaginary parts.

If we apply the imaginary operator to Euler's equation, we get

$$\text{Im } e^{j\omega t} = \sin \omega t$$

and if we assume that we shall always use only this operator with this exponential, we may write, simply,

$$e^{j\omega t} = \sin \omega t \tag{3-44}$$

Now we may rewrite Eq. (3-33) by setting

$$A \sin \omega t = A e^{j\omega t}$$

with the result that

$$T \frac{dy_s}{dt} + y_s = A e^{j\omega t} \tag{3-45}$$

Since we know from experience that the steady-state response of linear systems to sustained sinusoidal forcing is a sustained sine wave at the same frequency, we may take the solution of Eq. (3-45) to be given by

$$y_s = B e^{j\omega t} \tag{3-46}$$

where B now may be real or complex.

With this substitution in Eq. (3-45), and carrying out the indicated differentiation, there results

$$j\omega T B e^{j\omega T} + B e^{j\omega t} = A e^{j\omega t}$$

and therefore

$$B = \frac{A}{1 + j\omega T}$$

In order to eliminate the complex variable from the denominator of this expression and thereby separate the real and imaginary parts, we multiply numerator and denominator through by $1 - j\omega t$, which is the *conjugate* of the denominator.   Thus

$$B = \frac{A}{1 + j\omega T}\frac{1 - j\omega T}{1 - j\omega T} = \frac{A}{1 + \omega^2 T^2} - j\frac{A\omega T}{1 + \omega^2 T^2} \tag{3-47}$$

Now insert Eq. (3-47) in Eq. (3-46) and substitute for $e^{j\omega t}$ the equivalent complex quantity given by Euler's equation, $\cos \omega t + j \sin \omega t$. Expand the resulting expression, and group the terms into a real category and an imaginary category.   The latter category constitutes the steady-state sinusoidal response, since we are using the imaginary operator, and the result can be cast into either form of Eq. (3-42).
Thus

$$y_s = Be^{j\omega t} = \frac{A}{1 + \omega^2 T^2}(1 - j\omega T)(\cos \omega t + j \sin \omega t)$$

and expanding,

$$y_s = \frac{A \cos \omega t}{1 + \omega^2 T^2} + \frac{A\omega T \sin \omega t}{1 + \omega^2 T^2} + j\frac{A \sin \omega t}{1 + \omega^2 T^2} - j\frac{A\omega T \cos \omega t}{1 + \omega^2 T^2}$$

But only the imaginary terms are relevant; so

$$y_s = \frac{A(\sin \omega t - \omega T \cos \omega t)}{1 + \omega^2 T^2}$$

which may be written

$$y_s = \frac{A}{(1 + \omega^2 T^2)^{\frac{1}{2}}}\left[\frac{1}{(1 + \omega^2 T^2)^{\frac{1}{2}}} \sin \omega t - \frac{\omega T}{(1 + \omega^2 T^2)^{\frac{1}{2}}} \cos \omega t\right]$$

According to Eqs. (3-39) and (3-40), this equation is

$$y_s = \frac{A}{(1 + \omega^2 T^2)^{\frac{1}{2}}}(\cos \psi \sin \omega t + \sin \psi \cos \omega t)$$

or, as before,

$$y_s = A \cos \psi \sin (\omega t + \psi) \tag{3-42}$$

3-16   *Laplace transformation*

All the foregoing results for the dynamic behavior of process systems, including both the transient response and the frequency response, can be obtained by the methods of operational calculus.

The classical approach to the solution of linear differential equations with constant coefficients, which is employed in Sec. 3-11, involves three steps:

1 Solving the homogeneous equation to get the *complementary function*

2 Obtaining the forced response, or *particular integral,* from the nature of the forcing

3 Determining the constants of integration from the initial conditions

This method of solution becomes increasingly difficult as the order of the equation increases.

A shorthand, yet rigorous, method for solving these problems results from the use of operational techniques based on the Laplace transformation.

For our purposes we may regard the Laplace transformation as a relatively simple device for converting linear differential equations into algebraic equations so that the convenience of algebra may be used to solve differential equations. An analogous mathematical operation is the use of logarithms to effect multiplications and divisions by simple addition and subtraction.

Another important advantage of this transformation is that it permits a direct and convenient computation of the frequency-response characteristics of a system from the differential equations describing the system.

The Laplace transformation is identified by the symbol L. Thus the expression

$$L[f(t)] = F(s) \tag{3-48}$$

states that the Laplace transform of a function of time $f(t)$ is $F(s)$. Similarly,

$$L^{-1}[F(s)] = f(t) \tag{3-49}$$

states that the inverse Laplace transform of a function of $sF(s)$ is $f(t)$.

It is customary to designate transformed, or *s-domain*, variables by uppercase letters and time-domain variables by lowercase letters as in Eqs. (3-48) and (3-49). The quantity s is called the Laplacian complex variable.

The transformation is effected by multiplying $f(t)$ by e^{-st} and integrating the product from zero to infinity.

$$L[f(t)] = \int_0^\infty f(t)e^{-st}\,dt = F(s) \tag{3-50}$$

This equation has significance only if $f(t)$ is transformable. Fortunately, all the equations of practical concern to us are transformable. The criteria of transformability of a real function $f(t)$ are, first, that the function be defined and single-valued for $t \geq 0$; second, that all discontinuities be ordinary ones; and third, that the integral in Eq. (3-50) be convergent, that is, $\int_0^\infty f(t)e^{-st}\,dt < \infty$, for s equal to a number having a positive real part of σ (Sec. 3-18).

3-17 *Properties of Laplace transforms*

Some of the important properties of transforms are summarized in the following theorems:

1 Homogeneity:

$$L[Af(t)] = AF(s) \tag{3-51}$$

2 Additivity:

$$L[f_1(t) \pm f_2(t)] = F_1(s) \pm F_2(s) \tag{3-52}$$

3 Real differentiation:

$$L\left[\frac{df(t)}{dt}\right] = sF(s) - f(0) \tag{3-53}$$

where $f(0)$ is $\lim_{t \to 0} f(t)$ and $t \geq 0$ always.

Similarly,

$$L\left[\frac{d^2f(t)}{dt^2}\right] = s^2F(s) - sf(0) - \frac{df(t)}{dt}(0) \tag{3-54}$$

4   *Real integration:* Define

$$f^{(-1)}(t) = \int f(t)\, dt = \int_0^t f(t)\, dt + f^{(-1)}(0) \tag{3-55}$$

Then

$$L\left[\int f(t)\, dt\right] = \frac{F(s)}{s} + \frac{f^{(-1)}(0)}{s} \tag{3-56}$$

and similarly,

$$L\left[\iint [f(t)\, dt]\, dt\right] = \frac{F(s)}{s^2} + \frac{f^{(-1)}(0)}{s^2} + \frac{f^{(-2)}(0)}{s} \tag{3-57}$$

where $f^{(-2)}(0)$ is the double integral evaluated at $t = 0$. Both the real-differentiation and the real-integration theorems can be demonstrated by integrating Eq. (3-50) by parts.

5   *Final-value theorem:*

$$\lim_{s \to 0} sF(s) = \lim_{t \to \infty} f(t) \tag{3-58}$$

6   *Initial-value theorem:*

$$\lim_{s \to \infty} sF(s) = \lim_{t \to 0} f(t) \tag{3-59}$$

7   *Convolution integral, or Duhamel's theorem:*

$$L\left[\int_0^t f_1(T)f_2(t - T)\, dT\right] = L\left[\int_0^t f_2(T)f_1(t - T)\, dt\right] = F_1(s)F_2(s) \tag{3-60}$$

This theorem permits the determination of the inverse transform of $F_1(s)$, for example, by proper choice of the transform pair $f_2(t)$ and $F_2(s)$.

8   *Scaling:*

$$L\left[f\left(\frac{t}{a}\right)\right] = aF(as) \tag{3-61}$$

where a is a constant or function independent of t and s.

3-18   *Inverse transformation*

The principal advantage of the Laplace transformation lies in the fact that differential equations in time are converted into algebraic equations in the variable s.   These algebraic equations are manipulated until their inversion to the time domain can be done simply.   The inversion yields the solution of the original differential equation.

To facilitate this last step, a table of transform pairs is used.   Some frequently recurring pairs are listed in Table 3-1.

Table 3-1   *Condensed table of Laplace transforms*

$F(s)$	$f(t)$
$\dfrac{A}{s}$	A
$\dfrac{1}{s^n}$ $(n = $ positive integer$)$	$\dfrac{t^{n-1}}{(n-1)!}$
$\dfrac{1}{(s+a)^n}$	$\dfrac{t^{n-1}e^{-at}}{(n-1)!}$
$\dfrac{1}{s^2(s+a)}$	$\dfrac{1}{a^2}(at - 1 + e^{-at})$
$\dfrac{b}{(s+a)^2 + b^2}$	$e^{-at}\sin bt$
$\dfrac{s+a}{(s+a)^2 + b^2}$	$e^{-at}\cos bt$
$\dfrac{1}{(s+a)(s+b)}$ $(a$ and b real$)$	$\dfrac{1}{b-a}(e^{-at} - e^{-bt})$
$\dfrac{1}{s(s+a)(s+b)}$	$\dfrac{1}{ab}\left[1 + \dfrac{1}{a-b}(be^{-at} - ae^{-bt})\right]$
$\dfrac{s}{(s+a)(s+b)}$	$\dfrac{1}{b-a}(be^{-bt} - ae^{-at})$
$\dfrac{1}{(s+a)(s+b)(s+c)}$	$-\dfrac{(c-b)e^{-at} + (a-c)e^{-bt} + (b-a)e^{-ct}}{(c-b)(a-c)(b-a)}$
$e^{-Ts}F(s)$	$f(t-T)$

Example 3-2   As an example of how the table of transform pairs is compiled, compute the transform of the function $f(t) = kt$.

Solution   Substitute kt in Eq. (3-50) to get

$$L[kt] = \int_0^\infty kte^{-st}\,dt = \left[\frac{ke^{-st}}{s^2}(-st - 1)\right]_0^\infty = \frac{k}{s^2}$$

In the event that suitable transform pairs are not available for a particular problem, the inverse transforms may be obtained from the inversion formula

$$f(t) = \frac{1}{2\pi j}\int_{\gamma-j\infty}^{\gamma+j\infty} e^{st}F(s)\,ds \tag{3-62}$$

where γ is a real number $> \sigma$ (the exponential coefficient in the third criterion of transformability in Sec. 3-16).

For most process control problems involving transform equations which cannot be inverted conveniently, it is usually simpler to solve the differential equations directly by numerical methods rather than by use of the inversion formula on the transformed equations.

3-19   *Use of Laplace transform in process control*

The nature of many process control problems makes it possible for us to simplify somewhat our use of the Laplace transformation.

If, for analysis and design, we deal only with the perturbations in systems which are initially operating steadily, we may take the initial values of the dependent perturbation variable $y(t)$ and all its derivatives as zero. If, furthermore, the systems are describable by ordinary linear differential equations with constant coefficients, the Laplace transformation involves the following principal operations:

$$L[y(t)] = Y(s) = Y \tag{3-63}$$

$$L[Ay(t)] = AY \tag{3-64}$$

$$L\left[\frac{d^n y}{dt^n}\right] = s^n Y \tag{3-65}$$

$$L\left[\int y\,dt\right] = \frac{Y}{s} \tag{3-66}$$

The procedure for solving differential equations is to transform them to the s domain, using Table 3-1 whenever possible and Eq. (3-50) when necessary, and then rearrange the resulting algebraic equation into sums of terms in s which can be inverted to the time domain by inspection, again using Table 3-1.

Example 3-3 Find the response to step forcing of magnitude A for a first-order stage which is characterized by a time constant T.

Solution Equation (3-1) for this case is

$$T \frac{dy}{dt} + y = A \tag{3-22}$$

and transforming it term by term, assuming y and its derivatives are initially zero, gives

$$TsY + Y = \frac{A}{s}$$

or

$$Y = \frac{A}{s(1 + Ts)} = \frac{A/T}{s(1/T + s)}$$

This expression is of the form $1/(s + a)(s + b)$, where a is zero; hence, from Table 3-1,

$$y(t) = \frac{A}{T}\left[\frac{T}{1} (e^0 - e^{-t/T}) \right]$$

or as before,

$$y(t) = A(1 - e^{-t/T}) \tag{3-30}$$

Example 3-4 The temperature of the heating coils in a small polymerization kettle is increased suddenly from 100 to 200°C, and as a result the temperature of the molten charge in the kettle begins to rise from 100°C at a rate of 24°C/min.   Sketch the response of the thermometer in the charge if the behavior of the thermometer approximates to a first-order time lag or transfer stage with a time constant of 6 sec.

Solution   In this case the thermometer is forced by a constant-rate function, i.e., by ramp forcing, and the appropriate description is given by

$$T \frac{dy}{dt} + y = x(t) = kt$$

where y is the perturbation in thermometer temperature, and x is the perturbation in charge temperature.   Now transform this equation term by term, for $y(0) = 0$, to get

$$TsY + Y = \frac{k}{s^2}$$

Solve this for Y:

$$Y = \frac{k}{s^2(Ts + 1)} = \frac{k/T}{s^2(s + 1/T)}$$

and from Table 3-1 the inverse transformation is

$$L^{-1}[Y] = y = \frac{k}{T} (T^2) \left(\frac{t}{T} - 1 + e^{-t/T} \right)$$

or by rearranging,

$$y = k[t - T(1 - e^{-t/T})] \tag{3-67}$$

This is the general equation for the response of a first-order transfer stage of time constant T to ramp forcing at a rate k from an initial condition of rest.   For the particular case at hand, $T = 6$ sec and

$$k = {}^{24}\!\!/\!_{60} = 0.4°C/\text{sec}$$

Thus

$$y = 0.4(t - 6 + 6e^{-t/6})$$

The properties of this response can be identified by looking first at the initial slope, then at the condition for $t = T$, and finally at the condition after long time lapse, assuming the ramp forcing could continue.

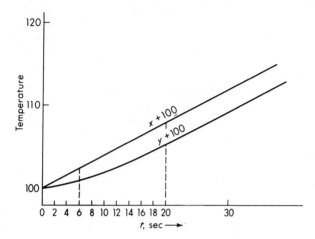

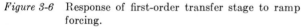

Figure 3-6 Response of first-order transfer stage to ramp
forcing.

The initial slope is

$$\left(\frac{dy}{dt}\right)_{t=0} = (0.4 - 0.4e^{-t/6})_{t=0} = 0$$

At $t = T = 6$ sec

$$y = (0.4)6e^{-1} = 2.4(0.368)$$

Since the forcing function x at $t = 6$ is $0.4(6) = 2.4$, the response
y is 36.8 percent of the forcing.

At large t, $y = 0.4(t - 6)$, which means that the response parallels
the forcing, with a constant lag in time equal to the time constant.   These
properties are shown in Fig. 3-6, with the ordinate scale showing actual
temperatures, obtained by adding the rest temperature of 100°C to the
perturbations.

3-20 *Transfer function*

The economy of expression that results from using the Laplace
transformation to express differential equations as algebraic equations in
s is epitomized in the *transfer function*.   This function, which completely
characterizes the dynamics of a linear system, is defined as the ratio of
the transform of the response to the transform of the forcing variable.
Thus, for the first-order transfer stage, the transfer function, commonly

designated $G(s)$, is

$$\frac{Y}{X} = G(s) = \frac{1}{1 + Ts} \tag{3-68}$$

This relation follows directly from transforming Eq. (3-1), assuming that the system is initially in a steady unperturbed state.

The transfer function may also be regarded as an operator, which by operation on the forcing signal produces the response signal.

3-21   *Frequency response from transfer function*

A particularly useful feature of the transfer function is the fact that the corresponding frequency-response characteristics of a system may be determined directly from the transfer function of that system by substituting $j\omega$ for s.   A demonstration of this fact may be made by showing that the same frequency-response characteristics are obtained from the transfer function as are obtained from the procedures used in Secs. 3-13 and 3-15.

Example 3-5   Compute the frequency-response characteristics of a first-order transfer stage from the transfer function for such a stage.

Solution   Substitute $j\omega$ for s in Eq. (3-68) to get

$$\frac{Y}{X}(j\omega) = G(j\omega) = \frac{1}{1 + j\omega T}$$

Separate this equation into real and imaginary parts by multiplying numerator and denominator through by the conjugate of the denominator, $1 - j\omega T$.

$$G(j\omega) = \frac{1}{1 + \omega^2 T^2} - j\frac{\omega T}{1 + \omega^2 T^2} \tag{3-69}$$

This complex function may be plotted directly on a *complex plane* for which the ordinates are imaginary numbers and the abscissas are real numbers.   The resulting plot in Fig. 3-7 for all frequencies is the same semicircle shown on the polar diagram of Fig. 3-5.

It can be seen that the magnitude ratio by the theorem of Pythagoras is the square root of the sum of the squares of the real and imaginary parts, namely, $\sqrt{\mathrm{Re}^2 + \mathrm{Im}^2}$, or

$$\sqrt{\frac{1}{(1 + \omega^2 T^2)^2} + \frac{\omega^2 T^2}{(1 + \omega^2 T^2)^2}} = \frac{1}{(1 + \omega^2 T^2)^{1/2}}$$

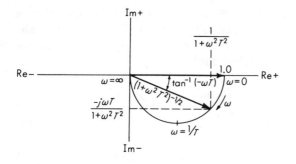

Figure 3-7   Frequency-response characteristics of first-order transfer stage on complex plane. Nyquist diagram.

and the phase angle is the arc tangent of the ratio of the imaginary part to the real part, or

$$\tan^{-1}\frac{\text{Im}}{\text{Re}} = \tan^{-1}(-\omega T)$$

At $\omega = 0$, the magnitude ratio $|G(j\omega)| = 1.0$ and the phase angle $\psi = \tan^{-1} 0 = 0$. At $\omega = 1/T$ rad/unit time, the coordinates on the complex plane, given by Eq. (3-69), are $1/(1 + 1) = 0.5$ for the real part and $-1/(1 + 1) = -0.5$ for the imaginary part. The magnitude ratio is $\sqrt{(0.5)^2 + (0.5)^2} = 0.707$, and the phase angle is $\tan^{-1}(-1) = -45°$.

At infinite frequency, the coordinates are 0, 0, and the magnitude ratio is zero, and the phase angle is $\tan^{-1}(-\infty) = -90°$.

A vector drawn from the origin to a point on the vector locus is the response vector for the frequency at that point and for unit forcing. If the unit-forcing vector on the real axis and the response vector are rotated counterclockwise at the particular frequency and corresponding phase angle, their respective imaginary parts (ordinates) projected on a time scale will trace the input and output sinusoids.

3-22   *Complex numbers*

Since the use of complex numbers in treating control systems offers conveniences and practical insights, it is advantageous to review briefly some of the important properties of these numbers.

A complex number is a number with a real part and an imaginary part. Thus the quantity $s = a + jb$ is a complex number having a real part a and an imaginary part b. Such a number can be plotted in a *complex plane*, or s plane, as in Fig. 3-8, wherein the real part is the abscissa and the imaginary part is the ordinate. Complex numbers may be expressed in three equivalent forms:

1 Rectangular, or cartesian, form, $s = a + jb$, or

$$s = |s|(\cos \psi + j \sin \psi) \tag{3-70}$$

where $|s|$ is the magnitude, or modulus, of s, equal to $(a^2 + b^2)^{1/2}$, and ψ is the argument, or phase, of s, equal to the angle with respect to the positive real axis, $\tan^{-1}(b/a)$.

2 Polar form,

$$s = |s|\underline{/\psi} \tag{3-71}$$

3 Exponential form,

$$s = |s|e^{j\psi} \tag{3-72}$$

The exponential representation arises from the fact that the Maclaurin expansion of $\cos \psi + j \sin \psi$ is identically the series expansion of $e^{j\psi}$, as shown in Sec. 3-15.

Additions and subtractions of complex numbers are handled in terms of the rectangular representation. For example, subtract $s_1 = a_1 + jb_1$ from $s_2 = a_2 + jb_2$ to get

$$s_2 - s_1 = a_2 - a_1 + j(b_2 - b_1)$$

Multiplications and divisions involving complex numbers are carried out most simply with the exponential form. Magnitudes are

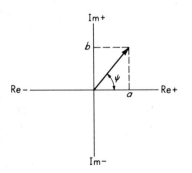

Figure 3-8 Complex-plane representation of complex number.

multiplied (or divided), and exponents, or arguments, are added (or subtracted). Thus, for

$$s_1 s_2 = (a_1 + j b_1)(s_2 + j b_2)$$

write

$$|s_1 e^{j b_1}| s_2 e^{j b_2}| = |s_1 s_2| e^{j(b_1 + b_2)}$$

To raise a complex number to power n, write the number in exponential form and raise each factor to power n. Thus

$$(a + jb)^n = (|s| e^{jb})^n = |s|^n e^{jnb} = |s|^n (\cos nb + j \sin nb)$$

The logarithm of the complex number $s = a + jb$ is

$$\ln |s| e^{jb} = \ln |s| + \ln e^{jb} = \ln |s| + jb$$

3-23   *Inverse Nyquist diagram*

For some problems it is advantageous to plot the reciprocal of $G(j\omega)$, namely, $1/G(j\omega)$, the forcing required to produce unit response, which, for a first-order transfer stage, is

$$\frac{X(j\omega)}{Y(j\omega)} = \frac{1}{G(j\omega)} = 1 + j\omega T \tag{3-73}$$

The vector locus of this function is a straight vertical line starting at 1.0 in the first quadrant as shown in Fig. 3-9. Now the phase angle is positive, or *leading*, and equal to $\tan^{-1} (\omega T)$, and the magnitude ratio is $(1 + \omega^2 T^2)^{\frac{1}{2}}$.

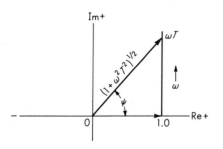

Figure 3-9   Inverse Nyquist diagram for first-order transfer stage.

3-24 Bode diagram

Neither the Nyquist diagram nor the inverse Nyquist diagram show frequency explicitly. The only way frequencies can be shown on these diagrams is by labeling selected points on the respective vector loci. This difficulty is avoided on the *Bode diagram* by plotting both magnitude ratio and phase angle as functions of frequency. Specifically, phase angle in degrees and the logarithm of the magnitude ratio are plotted versus the logarithm of the frequency. In order to plot phase angle and log magnitude ratio on the same linear scale, the magnitude ratio often is plotted in decibels, defined by

$$L = \text{log modulus in decibels} = 20 \log \text{MR} \qquad (2\text{-}8)$$

where MR is the magnitude ratio. Thus the log modulus for a magnitude ratio of 0.10 is $20(-1) = -20$ db.

For a first-order stage the magnitude ratio is

$$\left| \frac{Y(j\omega)}{X(j\omega)} \right| = \frac{1}{(1 + \omega^2 T^2)^{1/2}} \qquad (3\text{-}74)$$

At low frequencies, where $\omega \rightarrow 0$, the magnitude ratio approaches 1.0 (zero decibels). At high frequencies it approaches $1/\omega T$, and on a log-log plot, i.e., logarithm of magnitude ratio versus logarithm of frequency, the slope of the curve would be -1, since

$$\log \text{MR} = - \log \omega - \log T$$

With decibels as ordinate, the slope would be $20 \log 0.1 = -20$ db/decade increase in frequency, or $20 \log \frac{1}{2} = -6$ db/octave, i.e., -6 db for every doubling of the frequency.

The two straight-line asymptotes for the magnitude ratio, or log modulus, intersect at the *break frequency*, or *corner frequency*, where $1/\omega T = 1.0$, namely, at $\omega = 1/T$.

These characteristics are shown in Fig. 3-10, together with the phase angle. A rough approximation for phase angle is a straight line through the three points, $0°$ at $\omega = 1/10T$, $-45°$ at $\omega = 1/T$, and $-90°$ at $\omega = 10/T$, with horizontal straight lines at $0°$ for frequencies below $1/10T$ and at $-90°$ for frequencies above $10/T$. The straight-line approximations are shown as dashed lines in the figure.

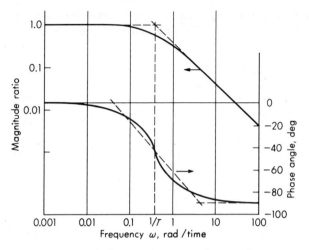

Figure 3-10 Bode diagram for first-order transfer stage.

3-25 Coupled first-order stages

Although a large number of real process elements and systems can be approximated by a first-order transfer stage, an even greater number can be approximated by the second-order transfer stage. The simplest example of a second-order transfer stage is a pair of coupled first-order elements. Consider the cascade of liquid-storage tanks shown in Fig. 3-11 in a process-flow diagram and in Fig. 3-12 in the corresponding signal-flow diagram.

If the y are the liquid heads above the discharge lines from the tanks, and if the volumetric flow rates through the discharge valves are linearly

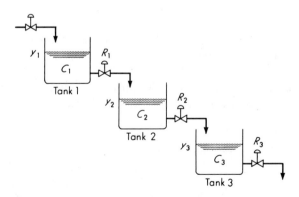

Figure 3-11 Cascaded liquid-storage tanks.

dependent on the pressure before the valves, simple material balances around the first two tanks lead to the following pair of equations:

$$C_2 \frac{dy_2}{dt} = \frac{y_1}{R_1} - \frac{y_2}{R_2} \qquad C_3 \frac{dy_3}{dt} = \frac{y_2}{R_2} - \frac{y_3}{R_3}$$

or, transformed and rearranged,

$$\frac{Y_2}{Y_1} = \frac{R_2}{R_1} \frac{1}{1 + T_2 s} \tag{3-75}$$

and similarly,

$$\frac{Y_3}{Y_2} = \frac{R_3}{R_2} \frac{1}{1 + T_3 s} \tag{3-76}$$

where $T_2 = R_2 C_2$, $T_3 = R_3 C_3$

R = resistance to flow = ratio of head before valve to volumetric flow through valve

C = tank capacitance = liquid volume required to produce unit change in head in tank

Since

$$\frac{Y_3}{Y_1} = \frac{Y_3}{Y_2} \frac{Y_2}{Y_1}$$

it follows that

$$\frac{Y_3}{Y_1} = \frac{R_3}{R_1} \frac{1}{1 + T_2 s} \frac{1}{1 + T_3 s} \tag{3-77}$$

This right-hand side of (3-77) may be regarded as being made up of a steady-state gain K equal to R_3/R_1 and an s-dependent, or frequency-dependent, part $G(s)$, equal to the product of two first-order-element transfer functions.

In general, the transfer function relating the terminal signals in a serial array of linear dynamic elements is the product of all the transfer

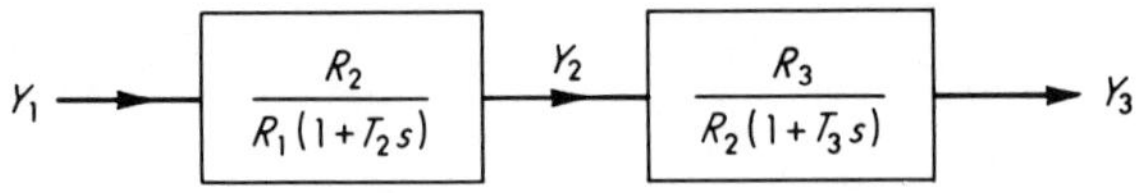

Figure 3-12 Signal-flow diagram for cascaded liquid-storage tanks.

units of the individual elements. Furthermore, the overall frequency-response characteristics are simply related to the characteristics of the individual elements. The overall magnitude ratio is the product of the individual magnitude ratios, and the overall phase angle is the sum of the individual angles.

Consider the two stages in Fig. 3-11. When the first stage is forced sinusoidally by setting $y_1 = A \sin \omega t$, the steady-state response from the first stage is $y_2 = A \cos \psi_1 \sin (\omega t + \psi)$. This response, in turn, is the forcing signal to the second stage, from which the response is

$$y_3 = A \cos \psi_1 \cos \psi_2 \sin (\omega t + \psi_1 + \psi_2)$$

The overall magnitude ratio is $\cos \psi_1 \cos \psi_2$, and the overall phase angle is $\psi_1 + \psi_2$, and these characteristics are, respectively, the product of the individual magnitude ratios and the sum of the individual phase angles.

For series of first-order transfer stages the ultimate slope of the overall magnitude curve at high frequencies on the Bode diagram is $-n$ on the log-log plot ($-20n$ db/decade increase in frequency on the log-modulus plot), where n is the number of first-order transfer stages in series. Also, the phase angle at infinite frequency is $-90n$ deg.

3-26 Interacting stages

In the system of Figs. 3-11 and 3-12, the stages are cascaded, and hence are noninteracting, in that what happens in tanks downstream in the cascade cannot in any way affect what happens in tanks upstream. Most sequences of elements in process systems, however, are interacting, and some care is required to keep track of the characteristic parameters.

A typical interacting system of two first-order stages is the thermometer element and thermowell shown in Fig. 3-13. This system con-

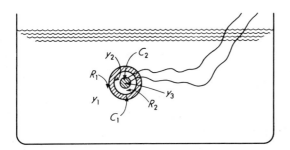

Figure 3-13 Shielded thermocouple (coupled interacting stages).

sists of a small silver sphere in which is embedded the hot junction of a thermocouple. Surrounding this sphere, but separated from it by a stagnant air space, is a metal sheath having a thermal capacitance of C_1 and a uniform temperature of y_2. The thermocouple and sheath are immersed in a stirred bath, which is at a temperature of y_1, and the surface coefficient of heat transfer on the outside surface of the sheath is such that the effective resistance to heat transfer is R_1. The thermal resistance of the stagnant air inside the sheath is R_2, the thermal capacitance of the silver sphere is C_2, and the temperature of the sphere is uniform throughout and equal to the hot-junction temperature y_3. It may be assumed that the thermal capacitance of the air is negligibly small compared with the other capacitances.

By an enthalpy balance on the sheath,

$$C_1 \frac{dy_2}{dt} = \frac{1}{R_1}(y_1 - y_2) - \frac{1}{R_2}(y_2 - y_3) \tag{3-78}$$

and for the sphere,

$$C_2 \frac{dy_3}{dt} = \frac{1}{R_2}(y_2 - y_3) \tag{3-79}$$

To find the relationship between the bath temperature y_1 and the thermocouple temperature y_3, the simplest procedure is to transform the two enthalpy-balance equations to algebraic equations and eliminate Y_2 between them. Equation (3-78), after transformation and collecting terms, then becomes

$$\left(T_1 s + 1 + \frac{R_1}{R_2}\right) Y_2 = Y_1 + \frac{R_1}{R_2} Y_3 \tag{3-80}$$

But Eq. (3-79) is

$$Y_2 = (T_2 s + 1) Y_3 \tag{3-81}$$

and inserting it in Eq. (3-80) gives

$$\frac{Y_3}{Y_1} = \frac{1}{T_1 T_2 s^2 + (T_1 + T_2 + R_1 T_2 / R_2)s + 1} \tag{3-82}$$

The equation for coupled noninteracting stages having respective transfer functions $1/(1 + T_1 s)$ and $1/(1 + T_2 s)$ is

$$\frac{Y_3}{Y_1} = \frac{1}{(1 + T_1 s)(1 + T_2 s)} = \frac{1}{T_1 T_2 s^2 + (T_1 + T_2)s + 1} \tag{3-83}$$

By equating the coefficients on terms having like powers of s in Eqs. (3-82) and (3-83), it is possible to find *effective time constants* identified by primes such that

$$T_1' T_2' = T_1 T_2$$

and

$$T_1' + T_2' = T_1 + T_2 \left(1 + \frac{R_1}{R_2}\right)$$

Thus Eq. (3-83) is appropriately descriptive of coupled first-order stages whether they are interacting or not. For the interacting case, the characterizing constants are the effective time constants.

3-27   General second-order system

The transient response of two first-order transfer stages coupled in series is given by an expression of the form

$$y_3 = B_1 e^{s_1 t} + B_2 e^{s_2 t} \tag{3-84}$$

where y_3 = output from second stage
  B_1, B_2 = integration constants, which must be evaluated from initial conditions
  s_1, s_2 = roots of characteristic equation of system
This characteristic equation for coupled stages with respective time constants T_1 and T_2 is given by the denominator of Eq. (3-83) as

$$(1 + sT_1)(1 + sT_2) = 0 \tag{3-85}$$

and the roots, therefore, are $s_1 = -1/T_1$ and $s_2 = -1/T_2$. Since these roots are real and negative, the exponential terms in Eq. (3-84) are non-oscillatory decay terms, and the transient response therefore disappears with increasing time.

Let us now consider the general second-order system where the roots of the characteristic equation are not limited to being real and negative as in the case of coupled first-order transfer stages.

Figure 3-14 shows a mercury-in-glass manometer, one arm of which is connected to a tank and the other arm open to the atmosphere. We know from experience that this kind of system will oscillate somewhat

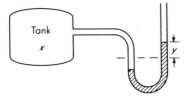

Figure 3-14   Manometric system.

when it is forced.   For example, if the tank pressure x is suddenly changed from atmospheric pressure to some fixed higher pressure, the reading of the manometer, y, will increase quickly, overshoot slightly, and then undergo damped oscillations, until the final steady value is reached.   It is instructive to examine how this behavior comes about.

A simple analysis of the forces acting on the system reveals that the forcing pressure is balanced by the sum of three forces arising, respectively, from the inertia of the mass of mercury, friction effects within the moving mercury and between the moving mercury and the glass wall, and the gravitational effects on the difference in vertical heights of the two columns of mercury.   Thus

$$x = mk_1 \frac{d^2y}{dt^2} + r_f \frac{dy}{dt} + 2y \tag{3-86}$$

where x = pressure in tank, in. Hg
$\quad\quad m$ = total mass of mercury
$\quad\quad y$ = height of mercury above zero pressure level, in.
$\quad\quad r_f$ = frictional resistance term, consistent units
$\quad\quad k_1$ = dimensional constant to express the inertial term in in. Hg

The transient characteristics of this system are defined fully by the homogeneous equation obtained by setting the forcing x equal to zero. Since there are only three terms in the homogeneous equation, each term may be divided by the coefficient on one term to reduce the number of constants in the equation to two.   What kinds of constants we choose are matters of convenience.   The following form is particularly useful:

$$\frac{d^2y}{dt^2} + 2\zeta\omega_n \frac{dy}{dt} + \omega_n{}^2y = 0 \tag{3-87}$$

The transform of this equation identifies directly the characteristic equation of the system, namely,

$$s^2 + 2\zeta\omega_n s + \omega_n{}^2 = 0 \tag{3-88}$$

In this standard form of expression for linear second-order systems, ζ (zeta) is the damping ratio, which is dimensionless, and ω_n is the natural angular frequency, in radians per unit time.

The solution of Eq. (3-87) is of the same form as that for the coupled stages, namely,

$$y = B_1 e^{s_1 t} + B_2 e^{s_2 t} \tag{3-84}$$

where B_1 and B_2 are integration constants, which must be evaluated from initial conditions, and s_1 and s_2 now are the roots of the characteristic equation (3-88). Since the differential equation is second-order, the characteristic equation is of second degree, and hence there are two constants of integration.

3-28 Step response of general second-order system

For the case of constant forcing, or step forcing, the general second-order equation becomes

$$\frac{1}{\omega_n^2} \frac{d^2 y}{dt^2} + \frac{2\zeta}{\omega_n} \frac{dy}{dt} + y = x = A \tag{3-89}$$

The steady-state response obtained by setting all derivatives of y with respect to time equal to zero is

$$y_s = A \tag{3-90}$$

and the total response to step forcing, then, is

$$y = A + B_1 e^{s_1 t} + B_2 e^{s_2 t} \tag{3-91}$$

By applying the quadratic equation to Eq. (3-88), we find

$$s_1 = -\omega_n \zeta + \omega_n \sqrt{\zeta^2 - 1}$$
$$s_2 = -\omega_n \zeta - \omega_n \sqrt{\zeta^2 - 1} \tag{3-92}$$

If $\zeta^2 < 1$, the roots s_1 and s_2 are conjugate complex, i.e., the roots are complex, but differ only in the sign of their imaginary parts, and if $\zeta^2 > 1$, the roots are real. It is convenient to consider these cases and two others separately.

3-29 Step response of overdamped second-order system ($\zeta > 1$)

If the damping ratio is positive and greater than 1, the two roots of the characteristic equation are negative and real, or $s_1 = -a_1$ and $s_2 = -a_2$, where the a_1 and a_2 are positive and real. Assuming the system is initially at rest or unperturbed, so that, at $t = 0$, $y = 0$ and $dy/dt = 0$, we have, from Eq. (3-91), after replacing s_1 and s_2 with $-a_2$ and $-a_2$,

$$y_{t=0} = 0 = A + B_1 + B_2$$

and

$$\left(\frac{dy}{dt}\right)_{t=0} = 0 = -a_1B_1 - a_2B_2$$

Simultaneous solution of these two equations gives

$$B_1 = \frac{a_2A}{a_1 - a_2} \qquad B_2 = \frac{a_1A}{a_2 - a_1}$$

and hence

$$y = A\left[1 - \frac{1}{a_1 - a_2}\left(a_1e^{-a_2t} - a_2e^{-a_1t}\right)\right] \tag{3-93}$$

which is the equation for two noninteracting RC stages in series, where a_1 corresponds to $1/T_1$ and a_2 to $1/T_2$.

This result also may be obtained readily by means of the Laplace transformation. Equation (3-83) is the appropriate transformed equation, with the substitution of A/s for Y_1 corresponding to step forcing of magnitude A. With some rearrangement, and dropping the subscript on the response variable, the transformed equation becomes

$$Y = \frac{A/T_1T_2}{s(s + 1/T_1)(s + 1/T_2)}$$

The inverse transformation by inspection of Table 3-1 is, after some rearrangement,

$$y = A\left(1 - \frac{T_2}{T_2 - T_1}e^{-t/T_2} + \frac{T_1}{T_2 - T_1}e^{-t/T_1}\right) \tag{3-94}$$

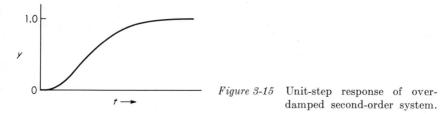

Figure 3-15 Unit-step response of over-damped second-order system.

Figure 3-15 shows a typical unit-step response for a system, like that depicted in Fig. 3-13, which is governed by an equation of the form of Eq. (3-94). Note that the initial slope is zero, and the point of inflection can be shown to lie at $T_1 < t < T_2$ for $T_1 < T_2$.

3-30 Step response of underdamped second-order system $(0 < \zeta < 1)$

If the damping ratio is positive but less than 1, the roots given by Eq. (3-92) are conjugate complex quantities, which may be written $s_1 = -\alpha + j\beta$ and $s_2 = -\alpha - j\beta$, where $\alpha = \zeta\omega_n$, the *damping factor*, and $\beta = \omega_n \sqrt{1 - \zeta^2}$, the *damped frequency*. The transient part of the response is

$$y_t = B_1 e^{(-\alpha+j\beta)t} + B_2 e^{(-\alpha-j\beta)t}$$

or

$$y_t = e^{-\alpha t}(B_1 e^{j\beta t} + B_2 e^{-j\beta t}) \tag{3-95}$$

To determine B_1 and B_2, note that, at $t = \infty$, $y_s = A$, and at $t = 0$, $y = 0$ and $dy/dt = 0$.

Since the total solution is

$$y = y_t + y_s = A + e^{-\alpha t}(B_1 e^{j\beta t} + B_2 e^{-j\beta t})$$

and

$$y_{t=0} = 0 = A + B_1 + B_2$$

then

$$\left(\frac{dy}{dt}\right)_{t=0} = (-\alpha + j\beta)B_1 + (-\alpha - j\beta)B_2 = 0$$

It is clear from this last equation that, for real systems, the integration constants must be complex whenever the roots of the characteristic equation are complex.

Simultaneous solution of the last two equations gives

$$B_1 = \frac{(-\alpha - j\beta)A}{2j\beta} \qquad B_2 = \frac{(\alpha - j\beta)A}{2j\beta}$$

and the total step response, then, is

$$y = A \left\{ 1 + \frac{e^{-\alpha t}}{2j\beta} [(-\alpha - j\beta)e^{j\beta t} + (\alpha - j\beta)e^{-j\beta t}] \right\}$$

Multiply through by j/j and rearrange to

$$y = A \left[1 - e^{-\alpha t} \left(\frac{\alpha}{\beta} \frac{e^{j\beta t} - e^{-j\beta t}}{2j} + \frac{e^{j\beta t} + e^{-j\beta t}}{2} \right) \right]$$

and since

$$\sin \beta t = \frac{e^{j\beta t} - e^{-j\beta t}}{2j} \qquad \text{and} \qquad \cos \beta t = \frac{e^{j\beta t} + e^{-j\beta t}}{2}$$

there results

$$y = A \left[1 - e^{-\alpha t} \left(\frac{\alpha}{\beta} \sin \beta t + \cos \beta t \right) \right] \tag{3-96}$$

Since $\sin \beta t \cos \psi + \cos \beta t \sin \psi = \sin (\beta t + \psi)$, we can rewrite Eq. (3-96) by multiplying the numerators and denominators of the terms in the inner parentheses through by $\beta/(\alpha^2 + \beta^2)^{1/2}$ and, by recalling that, for $\tan \psi = \beta/\alpha$, $\cos \psi = \alpha/(\alpha^2 + \beta^2)^{1/2}$ and $\sin \psi = \beta/(\alpha^2 + \beta^2)^{1/2}$, find that

$$y = A \left[1 - e^{-\alpha t} \frac{(\alpha^2 + \beta^2)^{1/2}}{\beta} \sin (\beta t + \psi) \right]$$

But

$$\alpha^2 + \beta^2 = \zeta^2 \omega_n^2 + \omega_n^2 - \omega_n^2 \zeta^2 = \omega_n^2$$

Whence

$$y = A \left[1 - \frac{\omega_n}{\beta} e^{-\alpha t} \sin \left(\beta t + \tan^{-1} \frac{\beta}{\alpha} \right) \right] \tag{3-97}$$

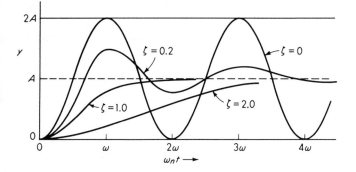

Figure 3-16   General-second-order-system step response.

This equation is sketched in Fig. 3-16 for $\zeta = 0.2$ and a single value of ω_n with time expressed in natural periods, namely, $\omega_n t$ in radians. The response is a damped oscillation with a damped angular frequency β, which is less than the natural frequency ω_n by the factor $(1 - \zeta^2)^{1/2}$.

3-31   *Critical damping* ($\zeta = 1.0$)

Also shown in Fig. 3-16 is the step response of a second-order system when $\zeta = 1.0$. In order to obtain the equation describing this response, note that, as $\zeta \to 1.0$, $\beta \to 0$ and $\alpha \to \omega_n$. Furthermore, as $\beta \to 0$, recalling for small x that $\sin x \to x$, $\tan x \to x$, $\omega_n \sin [\beta t + \tan^{-1} (\beta/\alpha)] \to (\omega_n/\beta)(\beta t + \beta/\omega_n) \to \omega_n t + 1$; whence Eq. (3-97) becomes

$$y = A[1 - (1 + \omega_n t)e^{-\omega_n t}] \tag{3-98}$$

This response is the critically damped response, and it is the same response that would be obtained with coupled first-order transfer stages having equal time constants each equal to $1/\omega_n$.

3-32   *Zero-damped response* ($\zeta = 0$)

For the case of zero-damping ratio, $\alpha = 0$ and $\beta = \omega_n$. Inserting these values in Eq. (3-97) and noting that $\tan^{-1} (\beta/\alpha)$ is $\pi/2$ for $\alpha \to 0$, we get

$$y = A \left[1 - \sin \left(\omega_n t + \frac{\pi}{2} \right) \right] \tag{3-99}$$

This response, also shown in Fig. 3-16, is the *zero-damped response* to step forcing. The amplitude of the sustained oscillation is equal to the magnitude of the step, and the frequency is the natural frequency. This case is not physically realizable.

3-33   Second-order parameters

The significance of the two parameters ζ and ω_n can be seen from the foregoing discussions. Damping in the system is measured by the damping ratio ζ. The damping contribution comes from the negative real part of the roots of the characteristic equation, which results in a response term $e^{-\alpha t}$. Since the damping factor α is $\omega_n \zeta$, the damping ratio ζ is the ratio of the actual damping factor for the system to the damping factor at critical damping, where $\alpha = \omega_n$.

The natural frequency ω_n is the frequency of oscillation for the zero-damped case, and it is the damping factor at critical damping.

In summary, for $\zeta = 0$, the system is zero-damped, and in response to step forcing, the response oscillates steadily at a frequency equal to the natural frequency ω_n and an amplitude equal to the step. For $0 < \zeta < 1$, the system is underdamped and undergoes a decaying oscillation with frequencies which decrease with increasing ζ. At $\zeta = 1.0$, the system is critically damped, and the response is the swiftest possible without overshoot. At larger values of ζ, the system is overdamped. Negative values of ζ correspond to instability and runaway.

3-34   Frequency response of general second-order systems

The frequency-response characteristics of the general second-order system are found in the usual manner by transforming the dynamic equation of the system and setting $s = j\omega$. From Eq. (3-87) the dynamic equation is

$$\frac{1}{\omega_n{}^2} \frac{d^2y}{dt^2} + \frac{2\zeta}{\omega_n} \frac{dy}{dt} + y = x(t) \tag{3-100}$$

and the transfer function for the system is

$$\frac{Y}{X} = \frac{1}{s^2/\omega_n{}^2 + 2\zeta s/\omega_n + 1} \tag{3-101}$$

The corresponding steady-state sinusoidal designation is

$$\frac{Y}{X}(j\omega) = \frac{1}{(j\omega)^2/\omega_n^2 + 2\zeta(j\omega)/\omega_m + 1} = \frac{\omega_n^2}{-\omega^2 + 2\zeta(j\omega)\omega_n + \omega_n^2}$$

We may separate this equation into real and imaginary parts by multiplying numerator and denominator by $\omega_n^2 - \omega^2 - 2\zeta(j\omega)\omega_n$ to get

$$\frac{Y}{X}(j\omega) = \frac{(\omega_n^2 - \omega^2)\omega_n^2}{(\omega_n^2 - \omega^2)^2 + 4\omega^2\omega_n^2\zeta^2} - j\frac{2\omega\omega_n^3}{(\omega_n^2 - \omega^2)^2 + 4\omega^2\omega_n^2\zeta^2}$$

from which the magnitude ratio, $(\text{Im}^2 + \text{Re}^2)^{1/2}$, is

$$\left|\frac{Y}{X}\right| = \frac{1}{\{[1 - (\omega/\omega_n)^2]^2 + [2\zeta(\omega/\omega_n)]^2\}^{1/2}}$$

and the phase angle ψ, $\tan^{-1}(\text{Im}/\text{Re})$, is given by

$$\tan\psi = \frac{-2\zeta(\omega/\omega_n)}{1 - (\omega/\omega_n)^2}$$

These equations can be written more economically by using a normalized frequency,

$$\Omega = \frac{\omega}{\omega_n} \tag{3-102}$$

Thus

$$\left|\frac{Y}{X}\right| = \frac{1}{[(1 - \Omega^2)^2 + (2\zeta\Omega)^2]^{1/2}} \tag{3-103}$$

and

$$\tan\psi = -\frac{2\zeta}{1 - \Omega^2} \tag{3-104}$$

It can be seen from Eq. (3-103) that the maximum magnitude ratio will occur near $\Omega = 1.0$ and its value will approximate $1/2\zeta$. As the damping ratio decreases to zero, the peak magnitude ratio increases to infinity. At the natural frequency the phase angle is $-90°$, and the limiting angle at infinite frequency is $-180°$. The magnitude ratio at high frequencies drops off at a slope of -2 on the Bode diagram (-40 db/decade), as is

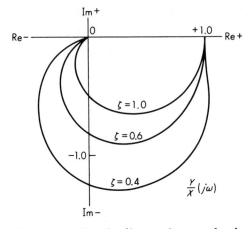

Figure 3-17 Nyquist diagram for second-order
            systems.

typical of a coupled pair of *RC* transfer stages.   Figures 3-17 to 3-19
show typical frequency-response characteristics on Nyquist, inverse
Nyquist, and Bode diagrams for various values of damping ratio.

3-35 *Estimation of system parameters*

Many process systems in their dynamic behavior resemble second-
order systems.   Feedback process systems often exhibit oscillatory

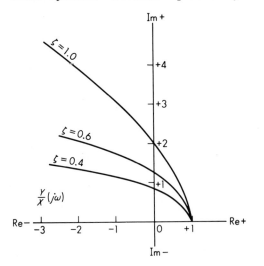

Figure 3-18 Inverse Nyquist diagram for
            second-order systems.

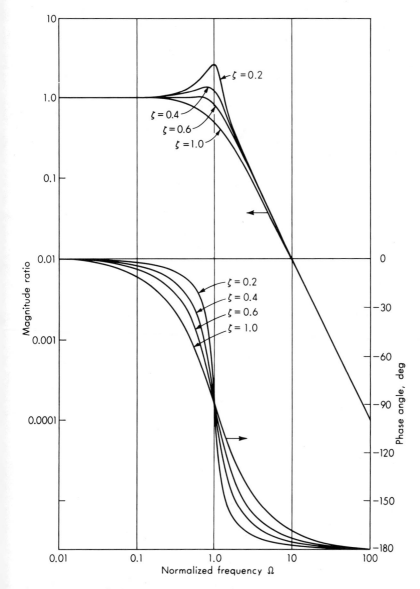

Figure 3-19 Bode diagram for general second-order system.

behavior when disturbed, corresponding to underdamping. For control systems, underdamping usually is the preferred condition. When the feedback arises from the recycling of process streams, the system, even when not in a control system, may still respond in an oscillating manner, but this condition ordinarily would not be desirable.

In the absence of feedback, many process systems behave dynamically as overdamped second-order systems. Typical examples of these systems are many kinds of heat exchangers, stirred-tank reactors, and liquid inventory systems, to cite but a few.

Although it is generally quite difficult to undertake a detailed and accurate theoretical analysis of an existing process system, it is often a relatively simple matter to identify from experimental data the properties of a mathematical model which will provide a reliable dynamic representation of the system. It does not follow that the experimentation necessarily will be easy. Frequently, considerable ingenuity is required to obtain useful dynamic data on a process system, but given reliable step responses and frequency-response data, the methods described in the next two sections will yield useful estimates of system parameters.

3-36   Estimation of parameters for overdamped case

For systems with dynamic behavior approximating that of an overdamped second-order system, the characterizing parameters are the two effective time constants of the system, T_1 and T_2. A number of schemes have been proposed for estimating these constants from the step response. See, for example, Draper, McKay, and Lees, or Caldwell, Coon, and Zoss, or Harriott.

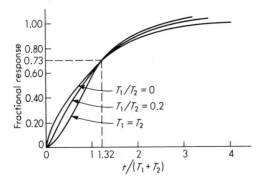

Figure 3-20   Normalized step response for overdamped second-order system.

If all possible step responses for second-order systems are plotted in the normalized form shown in Fig. 3-20, with ordinate as fractional response and abscissa as $t/(T_1 + T_2)$, it will be found that all the curves pass through a response of 0.73 at $t/(T_1 + T_2) = 1.32$. The limiting case, where $T_1/T_2 = 0$, is the first-order response, with the fractional response equal to 0.63 at $t/T_2 = 1.0$. The other limiting case is the critically damped response, where $T_1 = T_2$ and the point of inflection lies at $t = T_1$, or $t/(T_1 + T_2) = 0.5$, with a fractional response of 0.26.

If a step response has been determined for a particular system, it is a simple matter to determine $T_1 + T_2$ from the time required for 73 percent response. Then, by interpolation of the response at a shorter time on the family of responses in Fig. 3-20, it is possible to determine the ratio of time constants, and hence the individual constants. As an aid to that interpolation, Fig. 3-21 gives the fractional response for all possible time-constant ratios for $t/(T_1 + T_2) = 0.5$.

Example 3-6 A small metallurgical furnace is step-forced by increasing the gas-flow rate to the burners by 12 percent. The resulting temperatures are observed to be as follows:

Time, min	0	20	40	60	200
Temperature, °F	471	563	629	666	721

Estimate the effective time constants for this system.

Solution The percent response for each time is computed by dividing the difference between the observed temperature and the initial temperature by the total temperature change equivalent to the step, namely, $721 - 471$, or 250°F. Figure 3-22 shows the percent response. The time lapse for 73 percent response is seen to be 54.8 min, and hence $T_1 + T_2 = 54.8/1.32 = 41.5$ min. At $t = 0.5(41.5) = 20.8$ min,

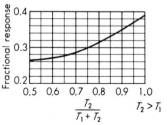

$\dfrac{T_2}{T_1 + T_2}$ $T_2 > T_1$

Figure 3-21 Second-order fractional step response at $t/(T_1 + T_2) = 0.5$.

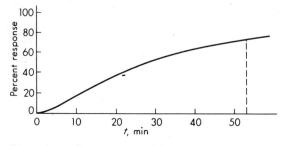

Figure 3-22 Step response of furnace.

the response is 38.0 percent, and from Fig. 3-21 at this response,

$$\frac{T_2}{T_1 + T_2} = 0.97$$

whence $T_2 = 0.97(41.5) = 40.3$ min, and $T_1 = 0.03(41.5) = 1.25$ min.

The two time constants for overdamped second-order systems can be determined also from experimental frequency-response data. For this purpose the Bode diagram is most convenient, since all that is required is the identification of the break, or corner, frequencies on the magnitude plot.

Example 3-7   Estimate the time constants for the system having the frequency-response characteristics shown in Fig. 3-23.

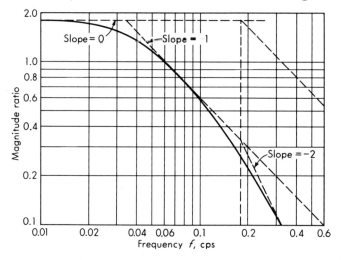

Figure 3-23   Magnitude ratio for second-order system.

Solution Three straight asymptotes having slopes of 0, −1, and −2 are fitted by eye as carefully as possible. The line of zero slope identifies the steady-state gain of the system as 1.8. Intersections of the other two lines with the steady-state gain asymptote give the break frequencies as 0.034 and 0.18 cycle/sec. The respective time constants, therefore, are

$$T_2 = 1/2\pi(0.034) = 4.7 \text{ sec}$$

and

$$T_1 = 1/2\pi(0.18) = 0.88 \text{ sec}$$

Note that the break frequencies must be expressed in radians per time when computing the time constants.

3-37 *Estimation of parameters for underdamped case*

For systems which are appreciably underdamped, having damping ratios ζ less than 0.5, it is a relatively simple matter to estimate the characterizing parameters ζ and ω_n from the step response. Figure 3-24 shows such a response for a manometric system in a flowmeter.

According to Eq. (3-97), the oscillations in the response must have a frequency of $\beta = \omega_n(1 - \zeta^2)^{\frac{1}{2}}$ rad/time, or a period of $2\pi/\omega_n(1 - \zeta^2)^{\frac{1}{2}}$, and the decay envelopes, shown by dashed lines on the figure, must be first-order decay curves with characterizing times of $1/\omega_n\zeta$. These two facts permit the determination of ζ and ω_n.

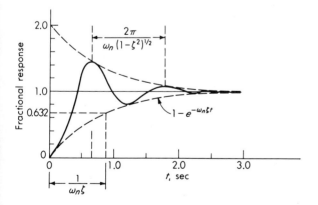

Figure 3-24 Step response of manometric system.

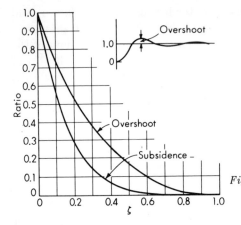

Figure 3-25   Damping ratio from over-shoot and subsidence ratios.

By differentiating Eq. (3-97), it can be shown that the fractional overshoot and the subsidence ratio are dependent solely on ζ.   Figure 3-25, which identifies these dependencies, provides a convenient means of estimating ζ.

3-38   Higher-order lumped-parameter elements

The process elements considered in this chapter are all *lumped-parameter elements* in that the characteristic constants in the dynamic equations for these elements are all presumed to obtain at specific points in the system.   For example, properties such as resistance and capacitance are not regarded as being spatially distributed in the system, but rather are taken to be lumped together at particular points.

In a strict sense, all real systems are distributed-parameter systems rather than lumped-parameter systems, since all real systems have some spatially distributed properties, and they all occupy space.   Nevertheless, the lumping approximation is valid for many systems, and it is used whenever possible to avoid the difficulties resulting from the manipulations of the partial differential equations required for most distributed-parameter systems.   Chapter 4 includes a treatment of some simple distributed-parameter systems.

From the discussions in previous sections we can infer the properties of process elements having lumped parameters and order higher than second.   The transient behavior of these systems will be dictated by the roots of their characteristic equations.   Since the degree of the characteristic equations equals the order of the corresponding differential equation, the number of roots is the same as the order.   Except for the case of inherently unstable elements, all real roots and all the real parts of

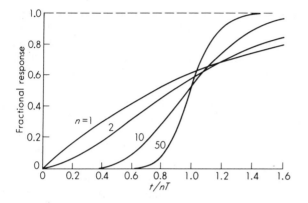

Figure 3-26   Step response for nth-order lag system.

complex roots will be negative.   Complex roots occur only in conjugate pairs, and each such pair contributes an oscillatory mode to the response. In general, the low-frequency pairs will dominate the response, and similarly, the real negative roots near zero, such as those contributed by large time constants, will exert a strong influence.

The effect of increasing order for systems without oscillatory modes is shown in Fig. 3-26, where fractional step responses for systems consisting of series of identical first-order transfer stages are plotted against a normalized time.   At very large orders n, the response has some of the properties of a *time delay*, inasmuch as there is a finite lapse of time between the instant the forcing is applied and the time the response becomes detectable.

As is shown in Chap. 4, it is possible to represent many high-order systems by relatively simple lower-order equations.

Problems

3-1   A plant survey made on a gas-fired oil heater includes a determination of the frequency response of the hot-oil effluent temperature to steady-state sinusoidal forcing of the gas-flow control valve, with results as follows for air pressure to gas-valve actuator cycling steadily at 8 to 10 psig and inlet-oil flow 120 gpm at 200°F:

Period, min	(Steady state)	10	2.5	1.0	0.5
Peak oil temp., °F	440	436	430	425	423
Min. oil temp., °F	404	408	415	419	421
Lag, % of period	0	5	22	51	92

Compute normalized frequency-response characteristics for this system and plot the results on Nyquist, inverse Nyquist, Bode, and magnitude-phase diagrams.   Note that the only normalization that can be done in this problem is the separation of the steady-state gain from the frequency-dependent magnitude ratio by dividing overall magnitude ratios by the steady-state magnitude ratio.

3-2 What are the natural angular frequency and the damping ratio of a second-order process system characterized by time constants of 2 and 4 min?

3-3 A liquid-expansion type thermometer is to be used as the primary sensing element in the control of a stirred-tank reactor.   As the bulb of this instrument, initially at 70°F, is inserted suddenly into the reactor when the latter is at a steady temperature of 240°, it is observed that the temperature indicated by the thermometer begins to rise almost immediately at a rate of 12°/sec.

If the control system can hold the indicated temperature within $\pm 1.5°F$, what excursions can occur in the actual temperature of the reactor?   Assume that the excursions are steady sinusoids at various frequencies.

3-4 A continuous stirred-tank reactor (CSTR) contains 500 gal of reacting mixture, and the feed rate to it is steady at 10 gpm.   If the reaction taking place is a first-order oxidation at low concentration levels with a rate coefficient k of 0.01 lb-mole reactant disappearing/$(ft^3)(min)$, (lb-mole reactant/ft^3), and if the mean feed-stream composition is 0.02 mole reactant/ft^3, what are the frequency-response characteristics of this system in terms of concentration of reactant in outlet and inlet streams?   Sketch the results on a Bode diagram.

3-5 *a.* Write the transfer function for a mercury manometer consisting of a glass U tube 0.443 in. ID, with a total mercury-column length of 22.4 in., assuming that the actual frictional damping forces are four times greater than would be estimated from Poiseuille's equation.

b. Sketch the response of this instrument when it is subjected to a step change in an air-pressure differential of 4 in. Hg if the initial steady differential was 1 in.

c. Sketch the frequency-response characteristics of this system on a Bode diagram.

3-6 A thermistor used as a thermometer in a gas duct begins to respond immediately when the gas temperature is changed suddenly from 6.6 to 14.9°C. At a gas velocity in the duct of 20 ft/sec, the rise time of the thermometer for 90 percent recovery is 7.1 sec.   When the gas velocity is 40 ft/sec, the rise time is only 3.0 sec.

a. What is the dependency of the surface coefficient of heat transfer between the gas and the thermistor on the gas velocity, expressed in the form $h = ku^n$?

b. At a gas velocity of 20 ft/sec, how long will it take the thermistor for 99.9 percent recovery of a step change in gas temperature?

3-7 For a general second-order system, show that the relationship between the subsidence ratio in, for example, the response to step forcing and the damping ratio and natural frequency is given by $\exp(-2\pi\zeta/\sqrt{1 - \zeta^2})$.

3-8 *a.* Using the Laplace transformation, determine the expression for the response to ramp forcing of a second-order system characterized by the parameters ζ and ω_n.

b. Sketch the response for $\zeta = 0.3$, $\omega_n = 0.02$ rad/sec, and the ramp $x(t) = -0.2t$ for t in sec.

c. What is the maximum displacement in time between response and forcing and when does it occur? .

3-9 *a.* Write the transfer function for a process element which can be approximated by three first-order transfer stages in series with respective time constants 2, 4, and 8 sec and a steady-state gain of 2.7.

b. Sketch the frequency-response characteristics for this system on a Bode diagram.

c. Compute the response for a step decrease of 10 percent in the input signal, and sketch the result for the first minute of elapsed time.

3-10 A feedback control system on a large fractionator responds to step changes in a controller set point for two different control-gain settings as follows:

For controller gain of 3.1, the response is not oscillatory and the indicated responses at 4-min intervals following the step are:

Time, min	0	4	8	12	16	20	2 hr
Percent of instrument scale	41.2	39.0	36.4	34.6	33.5	32.8	31.1

For the reverse step at a controller gain of 5.0, the response is a damped oscillation, with the first peak at a reading of 46.4 percent on the instrument scale in 13.6 min, and the second peak at 42.3 percent in 39.8 min.

a. What two effective time constants best characterize the low-gain case?

b. What are ζ and ω_n for the oscillatory case?

3-11 For the system of Prob. 3-4, write the differential equation relating concentration of the *product* in the effluent to the concentration of the *reactant* in the feed.

3-12 Derive an equation relating the heights of liquid levels in two tanks connected by a pipe containing an orifice if the liquid in the second tank discharges to the atmosphere through another orifice.

3-13 A well-stirred molten salt bath undergoes temperature cycles of $\pm 8.7°C$ at 500°C in a period of 5.8 min. Suggest a design for a vessel to be inserted in the bath, containing a spherical steel test cell of mass 0.8 kg and volume 300 cm^3. The salt is noncorrosive, and typical overall heat-transfer coefficients between salt and metal under the conditions of agitation in the bath are of the order of 200 Btu/(ft^2)(hr)(°F). It is essential that the test-cell temperature be constant within 0.05°C.

3-14 Prove that the substitution of $j\omega$ for s in the transfer function for a system gives the frequency response of that system. *Hint:* Write a generalized transfer function in factored form and apply sinusoidal forcing.

four

distributed-parameter process elements

The dynamic characteristics of simple lumped-parameter process elements were described in the preceding chapter. Although these elements may represent a substantial majority of the process systems normally encountered, there are a number of process elements which are important and for which a lumped-parameter characterization is inadequate.

In this chapter some analyses of typical simple distributed-parameter elements are presented. The pure time delay is included as a special case.

A general-process-system equation involving a maximum of five constants is identified as being quite normally representative of a wide variety of process systems.

4-1 Pure time delay

A commonly occurring and often troublesome process component is the *time delay*. This component differs from the time lag in that it holds signals back in time rather than merely attenuating them. A simple example is the *distance-velocity lag*, or *transportation lag*, which arises in a typical case when the actual point of measurement of some process variable lies downstream from the real point of interest. Figure 4-1 shows a fluidized catalytic reactor, the product stream from which is sampled at a point l ft from the reactor. If the product stream travels through the outlet pipe in plug flow at an average velocity v ft/sec, there will be a delay of l/v sec before changes in concentration within the reactor can be detected at the point of measurement.

At any instant of time the signal entering the distance-velocity lag will be $x = f(t)$. The signal leaving at the same instant of time will be identically the signal that entered l/v sec previously, namely,

$$y = f\left(t - \frac{l}{v}\right) \tag{4-1}$$

If the signal is modified in any way as it passes through the lag, the identity in Eq. (4-1), which is characteristic of a pure time delay, would have to be altered. An example is treated in Sec. 4-4.

For the purposes of analysis, consider the general distance-velocity lag in Fig. 4-2. The time constant for this system is the delay time $l/v = T_d$. Then $y = f(t - T_d)$, and this function expanded in a Taylor series is

$$y = f(t) - T_d \frac{df(t)}{dt} + \frac{T_d^2}{2!} \frac{d^2f(t)}{dt^2} - \cdots \tag{4-2}$$

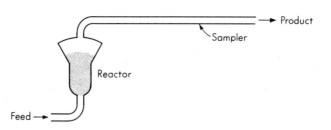

Figure 4-1   Distance-velocity lag.

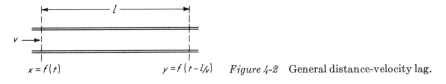

$x = f(t)$ $y = f(t - l/v)$ *Figure 4-2* General distance-velocity lag.

The Laplace transformations term by term at zero initial conditions are

$$Y(s) = \left(1 - T_d s + \frac{T_d^2 s^2}{2!} - \cdots\right) F(s) \tag{4-3}$$

and

$$X(s) = F(s) \tag{4-4}$$

But the parenthetical expression in Eq. (4-3) is identically $e^{-T_d s}$; hence, from Eqs. (4-3) and (4-4), the transfer function for a pure time delay is

$$\frac{Y}{X}(s) = e^{-T_d s} \tag{4-5}$$

4-2   Step response of pure time delay

For a step change in x of magnitude A at $t = 0$, the Laplace transform is

$$X = \frac{A}{s} \tag{4-6}$$

and from Eq. (4-5),

$$Y = \frac{A}{s} e^{-T_d s} \tag{4-7}$$

From Table 3-1 the inverse transformation of Eq. (4-7) is a step of magnitude A but displaced in time by T_d as shown in Fig. 4-3.

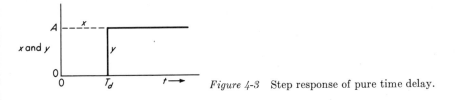

Figure 4-3 Step response of pure time delay.

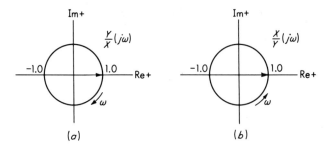

Figure 4-4   Frequency-response characteristics of pure time delay (polar diagrams). (*a*) Nyquist diagram; (*b*) inverse Nyquist diagram.

4-3   *Frequency response of pure time delay*

The frequency-response characteristics are found in the usual manner by substituting $j\omega$ for s in the transfer function of the system, giving

$$\frac{Y}{X}(j\omega) = e^{-j\omega T_d}$$

Since, by Euler's equation, $e^{-j\omega T_d} = \cos \omega T_d - j \sin \omega T_d$, the magnitude ratio, given by the square root of the sum of the squares of the real and imaginary parts, is $(\cos^2 \omega T_d + \sin^2 \omega T_d)^{1/2}$, which, from the trigonometric identity, equals 1.0, and the phase angle, given by the arctangent of the ratio of the imaginary part to the real part, is

$$\tan^{-1}\left(\frac{-\sin \omega T_d}{\cos \omega T_d}\right) = -\omega T_d$$

Nyquist and inverse Nyquist diagrams for a pure time delay are shown in Fig. 4-4. The Bode diagram is shown in Fig. 4-5, with the normalized frequency ωT_d as abscissa.

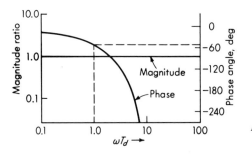

Figure 4-5   Bode diagram for pure time delay.

Both Nyquist diagrams are circles of unit radius centered at the origin of the complex plane. The magnitude ratio is constant at all frequencies, but the phase lag increases with frequency without limit. For convenience in sketching the Bode diagram, note that the phase angle is $-360/2\pi$, or $-57.3°$, at a frequency of $1/T_d$ rad/unit time. At twice this frequency, the lag angle is two times larger.

This unlimited phase lag is the undesirable characteristic of the pure time delay. It has the effect of lowering the critical frequency of feedback control systems, thereby making the control system slower in response. As is shown in Chap. 9, the time delay also is a destabilizing influence.

4-4 Modified distance-velocity lag

Many distance-velocity lags differ in behavior from the pure time delay in that they alter the amplitude as well as shift the phase of steady-state sinusoidal signals. If energy may be lost from the fluid traversing a distance-velocity lag, for example, there will be an effect on the magnitude and on the phase of the response to thermal forcing at the input to the lag.

Consider a reactor discharge line of length l and such wall thickness that the thermal transfer between fluid flowing through the line and the line itself appreciably affects the characteristics of the time delay. In this system the properties of resistance to heat flow between the pipe and the fluid and of capacitances of the pipe wall and fluid are distributed along the length of the line. Hence the analysis will be complicated somewhat by the need to include distance as an independent variable, in addition to time.

Figure 4-6 shows a section of the line. At a point z ft downstream from the entrance the fluid temperature is y, and at $z + dz$ it is $y + (\partial y/\partial z)\,dz$. The energy carried into the volume $(\pi d_i{}^2/4)\,dz$ by the flowing fluid is $C_p\rho(\pi d_i{}^2/4)vy$, expressed as enthalpy relative to fluid at $y = 0$. The energy carried out of the volume is $C_p\rho(\pi d_i{}^2/4)v[y + (\partial y/\partial z)\,dz]$. In these expressions C_p is fluid heat capacity, ρ is fluid density, d_i is inside

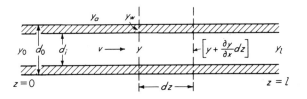

Figure 4-6 Section of distance-velocity lag with leakage.

diameter of the line, v is linear velocity of fluid flowing through the line, and ∂ is the partial-differentiation operator.

The net accumulation of energy in the differential volume is the difference between that carried in and that carried out less any energy lost from the fluid to the pipe wall. This last-named energy transfer is $h\pi d_i\, dz\, (y - y_w)$, where h is the surface coefficient of heat transfer for the fluid and y_w is the temperature of the pipe wall. Thus

$$\underbrace{C_{p}\rho \left(\frac{\pi d_i{}^2}{4}\, dz \right) \frac{\partial y}{\partial t}}_{\text{accumulation}} = \underbrace{C_{p}\rho\, \frac{\pi d_i{}^2}{4}\, v \left[y - \left(y + \frac{\partial y}{\partial z}\, dz \right) \right]}_{\text{net convection}} - \underbrace{h\pi d_i\, dz(y - y_w)}_{\text{transfer}}$$

or, collecting terms and calling $4h/C_p\rho d_i = 1/T_1$,

$$\frac{\partial y}{\partial t} = -v\, \frac{\partial y}{\partial z} - \frac{1}{T_1}\, (y - y_w) \tag{4-8}$$

Again, to simplify subsequent manipulations, we regard the process variables as perturbations about the normal steady operating levels.

As a further simplification, let us assume that the surface coefficient for heat transfer on the exterior of the pipe is high and that the thermal capacitance of the pipe wall is low. Then y_w will be equal to the temperature of the fluid surrounding the pipe y_a, and if this temperature is independent of distance, we may write $y_w = y_a(t)$.

Replacing y_w by y_a and transforming Eq. (4-8) gives

$$sY = -v\, \frac{dY}{dz} - \frac{1}{T_1}\, (Y - Y_a) \tag{4-9}$$

Thus the effect of the Laplace transformation here is to convert a partial differential equation to an ordinary differential equation.

Separating variables,

$$\frac{dY}{\left(\dfrac{1}{T_1} + s \right) Y - \dfrac{1}{T_1}\, Y_a} = -\frac{dz}{v}$$

and integrating from $Y = Y_0$ at $z = 0$ to $Y = Y$ at $z = l$ gives

$$\frac{\left(\dfrac{1}{T_1} + s \right) Y_l - \dfrac{1}{T_1}\, Y_a}{\left(\dfrac{1}{T_1} + s \right) Y_0 - \dfrac{1}{T_1}\, Y_a} = \exp \left[-\frac{l}{v} \left(\frac{1}{T_1} + s \right) \right] \tag{4-10}$$

For this system there are two forcing variables, y_0 and y_a, and one response variable, y, and hence there are two transfer functions relating the response to the individual forcings. The outlet temperature y_l responding to inlet temperature y_0 is given by setting $Y_a = 0$ in Eq. (4-10), on the assumption that there are no perturbations in the temperature of the surroundings. Thus

$$\frac{Y_l}{Y_0}(s) = \exp\left[-\frac{l}{v}\left(\frac{1}{T_1} + s\right)\right] = \exp\left(-\frac{l}{vT_1}\right)\exp\left(-\frac{l}{v}s\right) \tag{4-11}$$

The second exponential term on the right side of the equation is the transfer function of a pure time delay of l/v, and the first exponential term is a constant. Therefore the frequency-response characteristics at constant flow rate are a magnitude ratio of $\exp(-l/vT_1)$ for all frequencies and a phase angle of $-l\omega/v$ rad. The effect of the thermal leakage for this case is merely an altered but constant magnitude ratio.

4-5 Distributed-parameter forcing

The system of the preceding section is forced in a distributed manner when the forcing variable is y_a, inasmuch as this variable is distributed in space in the system. For this case the response of the outlet temperature to changes in the temperature of the surroundings is given by setting $Y_0 = 0$ in Eq. (4-10) and rearranging the resulting equation to

$$\frac{Y_l}{Y_a} = \left(\frac{1}{1 + T_1s}\right)\left\{1 - \exp\left[-\frac{l}{v}\left(\frac{1}{T_1} + s\right)\right]\right\} \tag{4-12}$$

If we call l/v the delay time T_d, we may write the equation

$$\frac{Y_l}{Y_a} = \left(\frac{1}{1 + T_1s}\right)(1 - e^{-T_d/T_1}e^{-T_ds}) \tag{4-13}$$

The expression within the first pair of parentheses is the transfer function for a simple first-order stage, and the expression in the second pair is a displaced distance-velocity lag with leakage. Substituting $j\omega$ for s in the latter expression and separating into real and imaginary parts via Euler's equation shows that the magnitude ratio for this system is

$$\frac{Y_l}{Y_a}(j\omega) = \frac{1}{(1 + \omega^2T_1^2)^{1/2}}(1 + e^{-2T_d/T_1} - 2e^{-T_d/T_1}\cos T_d\omega)^{1/2} \tag{4-14}$$

The numerator of the right-hand side of this equation clearly oscillates between $1 + e^{-T_d/T_1}$ and $1 - e^{-T_d/T_1}$ with increasing frequency.

Hence the magnitude ratio falls off in an oscillatory, or resonating, manner as frequency increases.

Similarly, the phase angle, which is given by

$$\psi = \tan^{-1}\left(-\omega T_d\right) + \tan^{-1}\left(\frac{-e^{-T_d/T_1}\sin T_d\omega}{e^{-T_d/T_1}\cos T_a\omega - 1}\right) \tag{4-15}$$

is also an oscillating quantity by virtue of the second term on the right-hand side of the equation. It is a bounded quantity, however, which, at high frequencies, is $-90° \pm \tan^{-1}(A/\sqrt{1 - A^2})$, where A is exp $(-T_d/T_1)$.

The resonating, or oscillatory, character of the frequency response is typical for distributed-parameter flow systems which are forced in a distributed manner. Figure 4-7 shows data obtained by Cohen and

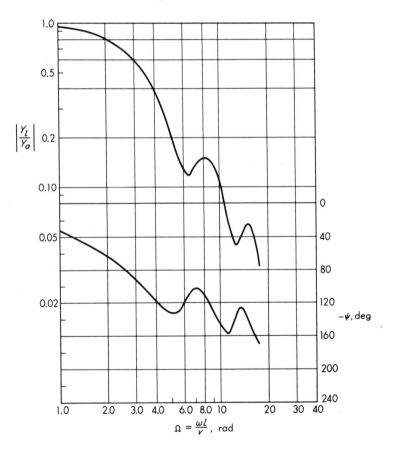

Figure 4-7   Bode diagram for distributed-parameter forcing.

Johnson on a simple double-pipe heat exchanger, in which the pressure of condensing steam in the jacket was the forcing variable, and the exit temperature of a steady stream of water flowing in the inner pipe was the response variable. The theoretically predicted behavior is given by the curves. Both magnitude ratio and frequency are normalized in this Bode diagram, the latter by multiplying the frequency in radians by the distance-velocity lag time of the water in the exchanger.

4-6 Ångström analysis

Many detailed treatments of the properties of distributed-parameter heat-transfer systems, of which the above are simple cases, are given in the literature. Indeed, the first quantitative use of frequency-response analysis as an experimental tool was made on a distributed-parameter system by the Swedish physicist Ångström in the middle of the nineteenth century. As described by Carslaw and Jaeger, a metal rod of unknown thermal conductivity was alternately heated and cooled at one end, and from measurements of the oscillating temperature at some distance along the rod, it was possible to determine the magnitude ratio and phase shift, and from these properties compute the thermal conductivity of the rod.

4-7 Tubular flow reactor

Consider the process in Fig. 4-8. A reacting fluid is moving at steady velocity v and in plug flow through a reactor consisting of a tube of length l. The process variable y in this case is the mole fraction of product B, which is produced according to the reaction $A \rightarrow B$ at a rate equal to ky_A lb mole $B/(\text{hr})(\text{mole solution})$. We can use one mole of solution as our basis for analysis because the reaction involves no change in the number of moles. For reactions involving changes in numbers of moles it is necessary to use a unit volume, or unit mass, as the basis for analysis.

A material balance on 1 lb mole of reacting fluid flowing

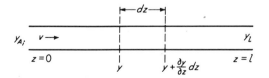

Figure 4-8 Tubular flow reactor.

through the differential distance along the reactor tube, dz, results in the equation of change:

$$\frac{\partial y}{\partial t} + v\frac{\partial y}{\partial z} = ky_A \qquad (4\text{-}16)$$

If $y = 0$ at $z = 0$, that is, if there is no product in the feed stream to the reactor, the relationship between the concentrations of A and B is given by

$$y_A(z,t) = y_{A_i}\left(0, \, t - \frac{z}{v}\right) - y(z,t) \qquad (4\text{-}17)$$

where $y_A(z,t)$ and $y(z,t)$ are the mole fractions of A and B, respectively, at distance z along the reactor and at time t, and $y_{A_i}(0, \, t - z/v)$ is the inlet concentration of reactant A at time $t - z/v$.

The Laplace transformation of Eq. (4-16) for zero initial conditions results in the ordinary differential equation

$$Ys + v\frac{dY}{dz} = kY_A \qquad (4\text{-}18)$$

The transform of Eq. (4-17) with all concentration terms identified at time t is

$$Y_A = Y_{A_i}\,e^{-(z/v)s} - Y \qquad (4\text{-}19)$$

where Y_{A_i} is the Laplace transform of the inlet concentration of A at time t, namely, $L[y_{A_i}(0,t)]$.

Eliminating Y_A between Eqs. (4-18) and (4-19) and collecting terms gives

$$\frac{dY}{dz} + \frac{s+k}{v}\,Y = \frac{k}{v}\,Y_{A_i}e^{-sz/v} \qquad (4\text{-}20)$$

The classical solution of a differential equation of this type is

$$Y = \exp\left(-\int \frac{s+k}{v}\,dz\right) \int \exp\left(\int \frac{s+k}{v}\,dz\right)\frac{k}{v}\,Y_{A_i}e^{sz/v}\,dz + C$$
$$\exp\left(-\int \frac{s+k}{v}\,dz\right) \qquad (4\text{-}21)$$

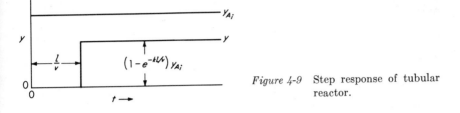

Figure 4-9 Step response of tubular reactor.

Evaluating the integrals from $z = 0$ to $z = 1$ and combining terms leads to

$$Y_l = Y_{A_i}e^{-(s+k)l/v}(e^{kl/v} - 1) + Ce^{-(s+k)l/v} \tag{4-22}$$

The integration constant C can be evaluated from the fact that $Y = 0$ at $l = 0$.

$$\frac{Y_l}{Y_{A_i}} = e^{-sl/v}(1 - e^{-kl/v}) \tag{4-23}$$

This equation is the transfer function relating product composition in the reactor outlet to reactant composition in the inlet.

By comparison with the transfer function for a pure time delay the step response must be as shown in Fig. 4-9.

Similarly, the frequency-response characteristics are a magnitude ratio equal to $1 - e^{-kl/v}$ for all frequencies and a phase angle equal to $-\omega l/v$ rad.

The foregoing results can be obtained equally readily by treating the system as a pure time delay in which the output signal is modified by the amount of reaction occurring in the time of the delay, l/v.

4-8 *Distributed-parameter process elements*

Additional examples of distributed-parameter process elements are presented as problems at the end of this chapter. The general modes of approach to all these problems are the same as those employed above. Partial differential equations are written to describe the dynamic behavior in an infinitesimal but representative volume of the systems. These equations are then converted to ordinary differential equations by using the Laplace transformation to eliminate time as an independent variable. The transformed equations are integrated over the spatial configuration of the system to get the transfer functions for the system. These functions may then be treated in a straightforward manner to obtain any particular responses.

4-9 *Parametric forcing*

The idea of parametric forcing was introduced in Sec. 3-12.   It is instructive at this point to analyze a simple example.   Consider the case of a distance-velocity lag in which there is thermal-energy exchange with the environment and a changing flow velocity.   With the usual simplifying assumptions of incompressible plug flow and radial-energy transport, the equation of change is the same as Eq. (4-8), which may be written

$$T \frac{\partial y}{\partial t} = -Tv \frac{\partial y}{\partial z} - y + y_w \tag{4-24}$$

where, as before,

y = temperature of fluid at time t and distance z along tube
y_w = temperature of tube wall
v = fluid velocity
T = characteristic time $C\rho d/4h$

where, in turn,

C = heat capacity of fluid
ρ = density of fluid
d = diameter of tube
h = surface coefficient for heat transfer from fluid to tube wall

Let the temperature and the velocity consist of a steady-state part and a perturbation, namely, $y_s + y$, $y_{w_s} + y_w$, and $v_s + v$, where now the y, y_w, and v are perturbations.   Insert these sums in Eq. (4-24) to get

$$T \frac{\partial (y_s + y)}{\partial t} = -T(v_s + v) \frac{\partial (y_s + y)}{\partial z} - y_s - y + y_{w_s} + y_w$$

Since $T \, \partial y_s/\partial t = 0$ and for small perturbations, $Tv \, \partial y/\partial z = 0$, this equation reduces to

$$T \frac{\partial y}{\partial t} = -Tv_s \frac{\partial y_s}{\partial z} + Tv_s \frac{\partial y}{\partial z} - Tv \frac{\partial y_s}{\partial z} - y_s - y + y_{w_s} + y_w \tag{4-25}$$

But at the steady state, v, y, and y_w are zero; hence

$$0 = -Tv_s \frac{\partial y_s}{\partial z} - y_s + yw_s \tag{4-26}$$

which may be subtracted from Eq. (4-25) to give

$$T \frac{\partial y}{\partial t} = -Tv_s \frac{\partial y}{\partial z} + Tv \frac{\partial y_s}{\partial z} - y + y_w \tag{4-27}$$

The solution of Eq. (4-26) may be obtained by separating the variables and integrating.

$$\int_{y_i}^{y_s} \frac{dy_s}{y_s - y_{w_s}} = -\int_s^z \frac{dz}{Tv_s} = -\frac{z}{Tv_s}$$

where y_i is the fluid temperature entering the tube; hence

$$\ln \frac{y_s - y_{w_s}}{y_i - y_{w_s}} = -\frac{z}{Tv_s}$$

and

$$y_s = y_{w_s} + (y_i - y_{w_s})e^{-z/Tv_s} \tag{4-28}$$

Differentiating with respect to z gives

$$\frac{\partial y_s}{\partial z} = -\frac{1}{Tv_s}(y_i - y_{w_s})e^{-z/Tv_s} \tag{4-29}$$

We may now eliminate y_s from Eq. (4-27) by inserting Eq. (4-29).

$$T \frac{\partial y}{\partial t} = -Tv_s \frac{\partial y}{\partial z} + \frac{v}{v_s}(y_i - y_{w_s})e^{-z/Tv_s} - y + y_w \tag{4-30}$$

By Laplace transformation at constant inlet temperature this equation becomes

$$TsY = -Tv_s \frac{dY}{dz} + \frac{V}{v_s}(y_i - y_{w_s})e^{-z/Tv_s} - Y + Y_w$$

which may be rearranged to

$$\frac{dY}{dz} + \frac{Ts + 1}{Tv_s} Y = +\frac{V}{Tv_s^2}(y_i - y_{w_s})e^{-z/Tv_s} + \frac{Y_w}{Tv_s} \tag{4-31}$$

Let $(Ts + 1)/Tv_s = a$, and since an integrating factor for Eq. (4-31) is $e^{\int a\,dz}$, the solution is

$$Ye^{\int a\,dz} = \int e^{\int a\,dz}\left[\frac{V}{Tv_s{}^2}(y_i - y_{w_s})e^{-z/Tv_s} + \frac{Y_w}{Tv_s}\right]dz + C \qquad (4\text{-}32)$$

where C is the integration constant.

Since $e^{\int a\,dz} = e^{az}$,

$$Ye^{az} = \frac{e^{sz/v_s}}{sv_sT}V(y_i - y_{w_s}) + \frac{Y_w}{Tv_sa}e^{az} + C \qquad (4\text{-}33)$$

Noting $Tv_sa = Ts + 1$, and for $z = 0$, $Y = Y_i$,

$$Y_i = \frac{V(y_i - y_{w_s})}{sv_sT} + \frac{Y_w}{Ts + 1} + C \qquad (4\text{-}34)$$

and at $z = l$, $Y = Y_l$, and calling $l/v_s = T_d$,

$$Y_le^{al} = \frac{e^{sT_d}}{sv_sT}V(y_i - y_{ws}) + \frac{Y_w}{T_{s+1}}e^{al} + C \qquad (4\text{-}35)$$

Subtract Eq. (4-34) from Eq. (4-35) to get

$$Y_le^{al} - Y_i = \frac{V(y_i - y_{w_s})}{sv_sT}(e^{sT_d} - 1) + \frac{Y_w}{T_{s+1}}(e^{al} - 1) \qquad (4\text{-}36)$$

For perturbations only in Y_l and V, $Y_i = Y_w = 0$, and the transfer function relating Y_l and V is

$$\frac{Y_l}{V} = \frac{y_i - y_{w_s}}{sv_sT}\exp\left[-\frac{(Ts + 1)}{Tv_s}l\right](e^{sT_d} - 1)$$

which reduces to

$$\frac{Y_l}{V} = \frac{y_i - y_{w_s}}{sv_sT}e^{-T_d/T}(1 - e^{-sT_d}) \qquad (4\text{-}37)$$

The frequency-response characteristics are given by

$$\frac{Y_l}{V}(j\omega) = \frac{A}{j\omega}(1 - e^{-j\omega T_d}) \qquad (4\text{-}38)$$

where A is a constant, $(y_i - y_{w_s})e^{-T_d/T}/v_s T$. Hence

$$\left|\frac{Y_l}{V}\right| = \frac{A}{\omega}\left[(1 - \cos \omega T_d)^2 + \sin^2 \omega T_d\right]^{\frac{1}{2}}$$

or

$$\left|\frac{Y_l}{V}\right| = \frac{A}{\omega}(2 - 2 \cos \omega T_d)^{\frac{1}{2}} \tag{4-39}$$

which is a resonating magnitude ratio oscillating between $2A/\omega$ and zero.
The phase angle is

$$\left/\frac{Y_l}{V}\right. = \tan^{-1}\left(\frac{1 - \cos \omega T_d}{\sin \omega T_d}\right) \tag{4-40}$$

This function, like Eq. (4-39), has been shown to identify the resonances in observed frequency-response data for double-pipe heat exchangers.

4-10 *General process system*

A typical process system will include a number of process elements such as first- and second-order transfer stages, time delays, and distributed-parameter elements. If it is desirable to represent an existing process system by an equation to be fit empirically, the most generally suitable form of that equation, expressed as a transfer function, is

$$\frac{Y}{X} = \frac{\omega_n^2 K e^{-T_d s}}{(1 + T_2 s)(s^2 + 2\zeta\omega_n s + \omega_n^2)} \tag{4-41}$$

Here the delay term with a delay time T_d takes care of distributed-parameter characteristics as well as pure time delays. The second-order term with damping ratio and natural frequency admits one oscillatory mode. The first-order term with time constant T_2 accommodates additional signal attenuation. Thus, by adjusting the various constants, this general-process transfer function can approximate the dynamic behavior of almost any process system.

The determination of the constants in Eq. (4-41) from dynamic-response data is made by the methods described in Secs. 3-35 to 3-37 after extracting the contribution of the time delay T_d, which is merely the displacement of the response along the time axis.

Figure 4-10   Unit-impulse representation.

In many cases it is not necessary to use all five constants.   If the forcing signal x is expressed in its equivalent potential values of the response y, the constant K, which is the steady-state gain of the system, is unity.   If there is no tendency for the system to oscillate, the under-damped second-order element can be eliminated.   Most of the commonly encountered process systems, in the absence of feedback control circuits and of internal recycle streams, do not oscillate.   Their step responses resemble those of overdamped second-order systems, and when their behavior cannot be approximated very accurately by a second-order transfer function, the addition of the pure time delay in the approximation usually provides a good representation.

Much of the early work in developing methods of selecting control-lers and adjusting them when installed was based on process representa-tions which included only the time delay and the first-order lag.   Some of these methods are discussed in Chap. 9.

Example 4-1   Estimate the response to unit-impulse forcing of a process system consisting of a pure time delay of 10 sec, a first-order lag of 20 sec, and a steady-state gain of 1.

Solution   The unit impulse is a pulse of unit strength and zero duration, which may be defined as the limiting area under the curve in Fig. 4-10 when $a \to 0$.

According to this definition, the unit impulse is given by the follow-ing equation:

$$u_0(t) = \lim_{a \to 0} \frac{1}{a} [u_1(t) - u_1(t - a)] \tag{4-42}$$

where $u_0(t)$ is the unit impulse, and $u_1(t)$ is the increasing unit-step function.

Transforming this equation term by term results in

$$U_0(s) = \lim_{a \to 0} \frac{1}{a} \left(\frac{1}{s} - \frac{1}{s} e^{-as} \right) \tag{4-43}$$

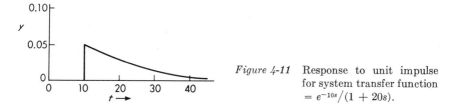

Figure 4-11 Response to unit impulse for system transfer function $= e^{-10s}/(1 + 20s)$.

Since $e^{-as} = 1 - as + a^2s^2/2! - \cdots$, the expression within the brackets for small a becomes $(1/s) - (1/s)(1 - as)$, or a and $U_0(s) = 1.0$; that is, the Laplace transform of the unit impulse is unity. Thus the response to a unit impulse is the inverse transform of the system transfer function. For this problem, then,

$$y = L^{-1}\left[\frac{e^{-10s}}{1 + 20s}\right] \tag{4-44}$$

From Table 3-1 we see that this is the inverse transform of $1/(1 + 20s)$ displaced 10 sec, along the time axis, which is

$$y = \begin{cases} 0 \\ \dfrac{1}{20}\dfrac{t^0 e^{-t/20}}{(0)!} = 0.05e^{-0.05t} \end{cases} \quad \text{for } 0 \le t \le 10 \text{ sec for } t > 10 \text{ sec}$$

This response is plotted in Fig. 4-11.

Problems

4-1 Calculate the frequency-response characteristics of a process system equivalent to a pure time delay of 10 sec coupled to a first-order lag of 20 sec and a second-order element for which the damping ratio is 0.5 and the natural frequency is 6 rad/min.

4-2 Sketch the characteristics computed in Prob. 4-1 on Nyquist, inverse Nyquist, and Bode diagrams.

4-3 It is observed in the course of a plant study that the concentration of rencillin in a continuous fermentor increases as tabulated below when the concentration of nutrient B is increased from 12.1 to 12.9 mass percent:

t, min	0	10	20	30	40	50	60	2 hr
lb rencillin/ lb solution	.040	.047	.063	.084	.106	.121	.128	.130

Write two different transfer functions to fit this system, one involving a pure dead time. Sketch the frequency-response characteristics for both functions on inverse Nyquist and Bode diagrams.

4-4 Derive the transfer function relating outlet-water temperature from a steam-jacketed pipeline to the steam pressure on the jacket. Assume that there is no axial heat transfer and that steam pressure in the jacket is independent of distance.

4-5 For the exchanger of Prob. 4-4 derive the transfer function relating outlet-water temperature to inlet-water temperature. Sketch the frequency-response characteristics for this case on a Bode diagram.

4-6 Repeat Prob. 4-5 for the case where the forcing variable is the inlet-water velocity.

4-7 A tubular flow reactor 16 ft long is used to effect an isomerization of Igorol A to Igorol C in the liquid phase. At a flow of 2 ft/sec, 40 percent of the incoming A, at a concentration of 0.1 lb mole/ft³, is converted to C in one pass through the reactor. Assuming the reaction is first-order with respect to the concentration of A, what is the transfer function relating concentration of C in the effluent to concentration of A in the feed? Sketch the response of effluent C concentration to a step increase in A concentration in the feed from 0.1 to 0.16 lb mole/ft³.

4-8 Sketch the frequency-response characteristics on Bode and inverse Nyquist diagrams for the system in Prob. 4-7.

4-9 A reactor discharge line consists of 24 ft of 2-in.-ID stainless-steel pipe through which a dilute stream of mixed acids flows at a velocity of 4 ft/sec. At the end of the line a liquid-expansion type of thermometer with an effective time constant of 3.2 sec senses the temperature in the pipe. If the ambient temperature is 60°F and the overall heat-transfer coefficient between the flowing fluid and the ambient air is 3.0 Btu/(hr)(ft²)(°F), based on the inside surface cover of the pipe, describe the observed temperature for the following behavior in reactor temperature:

   a. Sudden step from 160 to 184°F.

   b. Sustained oscillation between 160 and 184° at a period of 18 sec.

   Assume that the pipe wall is thin and that the dilute acids have essentially the same properties as water.

4-10 Derive the transfer function relating the temperatures of the two ends of an insulated bar of carbon which at one end is insulated and at the other end exchanges thermal energy with an agitated molten-metal bath. If the bar is of 2 cm² circular cross section and 20 cm long, what are the frequency-response characteristics on an inverse Nyquist plot?
   Data for carbon: Specific heat capacity 0.2 Btu/(lb)(°F), or cal/(g)(°C); thermal conductivity 0.01 cal/(cm)(sec)(°C); density 3.0 g/cm³.

4-11 What two time constants would best approximate the element of Prob. 4-10 via a second-order transfer stage and via the combination of a time delay and a first-order stage?

five

measurement and signal transmission

The quality of performance of feedback control systems is directly dependent on the quality of measurement of the controlled process variables. One of the most critical problems in designing process control systems is often the specification of the sensing devices for obtaining significant measures of the actual process variables to be controlled.

In this chapter the common methods of measuring the principal process variables are described briefly. Dynamic characteristics of typical sensors are given in terms of the basic transfer functions discussed in Chaps. 3 and 4. In addition, the elements used for transmitting signals and the dynamic characteristics of these elements are treated in sufficient detail to identify the bases for choosing particular transmission systems.

5-1   Process variables

The principal process variables, approximately in descending order of the frequency of their occurrence in process systems, are *temperature, pressure, flow rate, composition,* and *liquid level*.   Some of these variables, such as pressure, can be measured relatively directly.   Others, such as temperature, can be measured only indirectly.   Often the indirect measures are made by measuring another process variable.   Indeed, all five process variables can be measured by means of a pressure measurement.

5-2   Selection of sensing devices

Before considering the particular methods of measuring the different process variables, it is useful to examine the important factors which govern, generally, the selection of measuring instruments.   There are no hard-and-fast rules for making this selection, but the possibilities for choice can be narrowed appreciably by considering, first, a few factors. The following questions identify the more important of these factors:

1   What variable is the best measure of the condition to be controlled in the system?

2   What range does the variable cover normally, and what extreme range occasionally?

3   What is to be done with the information from the instrument? Is it to be indicated or recorded?

4   What accuracy, precision, and sensitivity of measurement are required?

5   What response speeds and what kinds of responses are desirable?

6   Are there process hazards such as corrosive fluids, sludging, or flammable and explosive mixtures at the points of measurement?

7   What is the location of the primary sensing element, and are there problems of size and shape of installation or remoteness requiring extensive transmission of signals associated with this location?

8   What reliability is needed?   Are there special requirements of ruggedness, availability of parts, and freedom from maintenance?

9   What is the cost, including first cost and operating cost, delivery times, and the like?

Obviously, the principal factors in choosing instruments are concerned with the process itself.   It is axiomatic that the design of process control systems requires, first of all, a clear grasp of the processes involved.

The actual choices of instruments almost always involve compromises among the important factors.   In some cases, other factors, not explicit in the list of questions above, become of overriding importance. For example, the most important factor in selecting a complicated and costly instrument for measuring chemical composition might be the quality of service provided by the manufacturer of the instrument.

The most useful sources of practical information on process instruments of all kinds are the instrument manufacturers themselves.   They provide technical literature and engineering advice, and they conduct clinics and seminars related to the selection and use of their products. Their helpfulness, however, does not relieve the process engineer of the responsibility of being familiar with the general properties of measuring instruments and with the principal methods of measurement.

5-3   *Accuracy and precision*

The *accuracy* of a measurement is the closeness with which the measure approaches the true value of the variable being measured. *Precision*, on the other hand, is the reproducibility with which repeated measures of the same variable can be made under identical conditions.   From the standpoint of automatic process control, the latter property usually is more important than the former.   That is, it is usually more desirable to measure a variable precisely than it is to have a high degree of absolute accuracy.

An example of the distinction between these two properties of measurement is shown in Fig. 5-1.   The dashed curve shows the behavior in time of the true temperature of a gas.   Line *A* is the measure of this temperature by a precise but inaccurate instrument, and line *B* is the

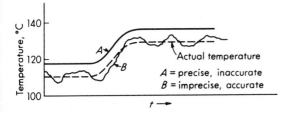

Figure 5-1   Accuracy and precision in temperature measurement.

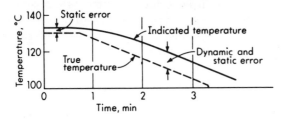

Figure 5-2   Static and dynamic error.

measure by an imprecise but more accurate instrument.   The former
instrument has greater error; the latter has greater *drift*.

Two kinds of accuracy are distinguished, namely, *static, or steady-
state, accuracy* and *dynamic accuracy*.   Static accuracy is the closeness of
approach to the true value of the variable when the true value is constant
in time.   Dynamic accuracy is the closeness of approach of the measure
when the true value is changing with time.   Since the numerical value
of the dynamic accuracy will depend on the nature of the time variation
of the true value of the variable being measured, as well as on the properties of the measuring system, it is necessary to specify this time variation, along with a specification of dynamic accuracy.   For process control
systems a practical specification of the time variation is ramp forcing and
a practical designation of the dynamic accuracy is the *dynamic error*
resulting from this forcing.   Figure 5-2 shows the dynamic and static
errors of a thermometric system when forced by a ramp of $-10°C/\text{min}$.
In this example the dynamic error is zero at the start of the ramp, and
then it increases to a constant value.   For a first-order transfer stage the
constant value of the dynamic error is given by the product of the ramp
slope and the time constant of the stage.

5-4   *Sensitivity*

The sensitivity of a measuring element is defined by the ratio of
the output-signal change to the change in measured variable.   The greater
the output-signal change for a given input change, the greater is the
sensitivity.

This quantity is the steady-state ratio, and hence it is equivalent
to the steady-state gain of the element, which is the magnitude ratio of
the frequency response at zero frequency.   It is expressed either in dimensional form, as, for example, 0.1 in. of indicator travel per degree Fahren-
heit, or in normalized form as a ratio of percentages.

There is another kind of sensitivity which is an important property of real measuring systems.   This sensitivity is expressed as the smallest change in the measured variable which will produce a change in the output signal from the sensing element.   For many physical systems, particularly those which contain sequences of levers and linkages, there are tendencies for moving parts to stick and to have some free play, with the result that input signals smaller than some threshold magnitude do not produce any detectable output signal.   For well-designed and constructed instruments this sensitivity will be high, as reflected in the ability to respond to very small changes in the process variable.

5-5 Speed and nature of response

The speed of response of sensing devices may be expressed or specified in terms of the measures described in Chap. 2, such as the rise time or the settling time of the step response.   For relatively simple elements the value of the principal time constant is a practical index, and it is probably the one most widely used by instrument manufacturers.   The most informative expression, of course, is the transfer function of the element.

It is important to remember that the dynamic character of a measuring device as reflected in measures like the response speed often depends as much on the location of the sensing element in the process equipment as it does on the particular properties of the element itself.   The time constant of a particular thermometer in a boiling liquid, for example, will be much less than the time constant of the same thermometer in a slow-moving gas stream.

For most measuring instruments the desired nature, or form, of response is that of a second-order system which is slightly underdamped. A damping ratio of 0.5 or 0.6 produces a step response with a relatively short rise time and a barely detectable overshoot.   Smaller damping ratios result in excessive oscillation following perturbations, and larger ratios are too sluggish.

5-6 Pressure

Pressure is defined as the ratio of force to the area over which the force is applied.   Most pressure meters measure the force directly by identifying the countervailing force required to balance the pressure.

In the normal ranges of pressure there are four types of meters in principal use.   The type depends on whether the pressure is balanced by (1) a liquid column, (2) a spring outside of the pressurized system, (3) the elastic deformation of the pressurized system, or (4) a pneumatic pressure.

For information on sensors suitable for measuring extremely low pressures and extremely high pressures, consult the references listed in the bibliography.

5-7   *Pressure balanced by liquid column*

This class of pressure sensors includes (1) the liquid manometer, (2) liquid-column barometers, (3) draft gauges which are inclined manometers, (4) two-liquid, or differential, manometers, (5) well manometers, (6) enlarged leg manometers, and (7) bell differential-pressure meters. These instruments are shown sketched in Fig. 5-3, with corresponding numbers.

The first five of these sensors are not ordinarily used as primary sensors in automatic feedback circuits, but they are widely used as auxiliary sensors in process systems for indicating low to moderate pressures and differential pressures. The last two generate signals which can be used in controlling instruments, and hence both are used as primary sensors for automatic control.

In the enlarged leg manometer the diameter of the range tube determines the range; the restriction screw adjusts the damping. The

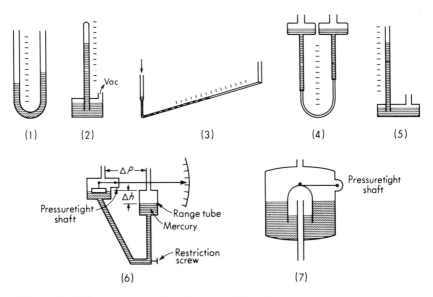

Figure 5-3   Pressure sensors, liquid-column balancing.

output signal from this instrument and from the bell meter is usually an angular displacement of the shaft connected to the float.

The enlarged leg manometer is used, principally, for measuring the pressure drops across orifices for flowmeters. It has typical differential pressure ranges of from 10 to 600 in. of water at static pressures up to 5,000 psi.

The bell meter is used for low differential pressures of the order of 1 to 15 in. water. Large bell floats generate large forces for long mechanical transmission of responses. The bell design affords protection against damage from overranging pressures and from flow reversal.

5-8   Pressure balanced by external spring

In these instruments the pressure is applied to either a thin metal diaphragm or a limp leather, rubber, or plastic diaphragm, loaded by an outside spring, usually flat. The metal-diaphragm elements sense pressures up to 5 psi, and the limp diaphragms may be used for total pressures up to 20 in. water and maximum sensitivities up to 0.2 in. water for full range.

Diagrams of typical examples of this class of pressure sensors are shown in Fig. 5-4.

5-9   Pressure balanced by elastic deformation of pressurized system

This class of pressure sensors includes the most widely used pressure gauges. The principal types are the pressure springs, such as the bourdon

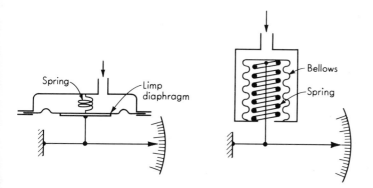

Figure 5-4   Pressure sensors, external-spring balancing.

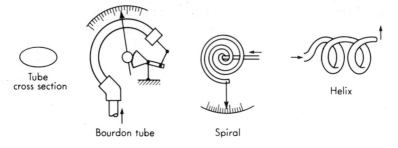

Tube
cross section

Bourdon tube   Spiral   Helix

Figure 5-5   Pressure springs.

tube, the spiral, and the helix, and the bellows and diaphragm gauges.
The strain gauge described in Sec. 5-11 may be regarded as a special case.

Pressure springs are shaped as shown in Fig. 5-5.   They all have
hollow elliptical cross sections which tend to become circular with increasing pressure on the inside, and hence tend to straighten out.   Since one
end of the tube is fixed, the movement of the other end is a measure of the
pressure inside the tube.

Pressure springs may be used for pressures in excess of 50,000 psi.
The spiral and helix are used where greater sensitivity is required.

The bellows pressure element as shown in Fig. 5-6 normally is used
in the pressure range from 5 in. water to 100 psi.   These elements sometimes are coupled in pairs for absolute or for differential-pressure
measurement.

For higher pressures the bellows may be loaded by an outside spring,
in which case they fall in the preceding category of pressure-gauge types.

5-10   *Pneumatic-balance pressure measurement*

A popular pressure gauge characterized by high speed of response,
low dead zone, and convenient output signal is the pneumatic-balance
type of sensor.   This instrument is particularly widely used for measuring
differential pressures.   Figure 5-7 is a simple diagram of the differential

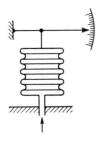

Figure 5-6   Bellows-pressure element.

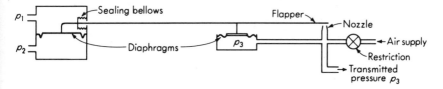

Figure 5-7   Pneumatic differential-pressure cell.

instrument, and Fig. 5-8 shows the same principle applied in a simple design for sensing a single pressure.

In both these instruments an accurate correspondence between output signal and input signal is attained by the use of high gain amplification and negative feedback.   Since the principle is widely used in pneumatic signal transmission and generation, we examine, briefly, what is involved.

A rise in the pressure differential $p_2 - p_1$ in Fig. 5-7 results in an upward displacement of the diaphragm separating the two pressure volumes.   The arm connected to the diaphragm pivots at the sealing bellows and forces the flapper to move closer to the nozzle, thereby reducing the flow of air which continually escapes the nozzle.   Since a restricted flow of air supplies the nozzle system, the air pressure within that system depends on the flow rate from the nozzle, and as the escape flow is decreased, the pressure rises.   This pressure is not only the output signal from the sensor but also the source of the negative feedback, and as it rises, it moves the flapper away from the nozzle by means of the diaphragm connected at an intermediate point on the flapper arm.   At balance the flapper will occupy a position in respect to the nozzle which will result in an output pressure proportional to the input differential pressure.   For accurate proportionality the essential requirement is that the signal amplification in the flapper-nozzle system be large; that is, a minute travel in the flapper should produce a large change in the transmitted air pressure.

This requirement can be shown best by a simplified formal analysis of the system.   The position of the flapper, z, depends on the difference in displacements resulting from the input differential pressure and the

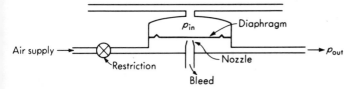

Figure 5-8   Pneumatic pressure gauge.

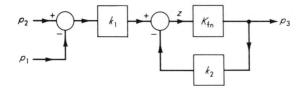

Figure 5-9   Signal-flow diagram for differential-pressure cell.

output pressure on the feedback diaphragm.   Thus

$$(p_2 - p_1)k_1 - p_3k_2 = z \tag{5-1}$$

where $p_2 - p_1$ = input differential pressure
$\qquad p_3$ = output pressure
$\qquad k_1, k_2$ = constants accommodating diaphragm areas, lever
$\qquad\qquad$ advantages, and elastic moduli of diaphragms
$\qquad$ If we neglect for this analysis the resistance-capacitance lag in the
flapper-nozzle system,

$$p_3 = K_{fn}z \tag{5-2}$$

where K_{fn} is the gain of the flapper-nozzle system.
$\qquad$ Eliminating z between Eqs. (5-1) and (5-2) and collecting terms
gives

$$p_3\left(k_2 + \frac{1}{K_{fn}}\right) = (p_2 - p_1)k_1$$

and if $K_{fn} \gg 1$,

$$p_3 = \frac{k_1}{k_2}(p_2 - p_1) \tag{5-3}$$

Thus the output signal from the differential-pressure cell is directly proportional to the input differential pressure and independent of the flapper-
nozzle gain.   A simple block diagram for this system is shown in Fig. 5-9.

5-11 *Pressure measurement by strain gauge*

An important and relatively new pressure transducer consists of a
sensitive electric strain gauge mounted on an element which expands

when pressurized internally. The strain gauge is essentially many lengths of a fine resistance wire which, since it increases in resistance when stretched, affords a convenient measure of the elastic deformation of the pressurized element, and hence a measure of the pressure. These instruments are accurate and precise; their response is rapid; and their useful range extends to pressures of thousands of atmospheres.

5-12 Pressure-sensor response

The dynamic response of pressure sensors is generally characterizable by the slightly underdamped second-order response. Rise times for 10 to 90 percent recovery from step forcing may run as long as 10 to 20 sec for a heavily damped enlarged leg manometer, but for most of the sensors described above the rise times will be less than 1 sec.

5-13 Temperature

Temperature is the most important process variable, but it is also, perhaps, the most difficult to measure. It is used sometimes as a measure of composition and sometimes as the principal control variable for chemical-reaction rate, product yield, human comfort, and countless other properties.

Unlike pressure, temperature cannot be measured directly. It must be inferred from its effect on volume, pressure, electromotive force, electric resistance, radiation intensity, and so on.

Temperature measurement below 500°C (932°F) is called *thermometry*, and above that temperature it is called *pyrometry*. The five chief methods of measurement are based on the properties of expansion, state of aggregation, electric resistance, thermoelectric potential, and radiation intensity.

The difficulties in measuring temperatures arise primarily from the fact that there are so many carriers for thermal energy. Consider a temperature sensor mounted in a hot gas stream flowing along a pipe. In a steady-state condition all thermal fluxes and all temperatures will be constant in time, but the actual temperature of the gas near the sensor may be quite different from the temperature of the sensor. If the walls of the pipe are cooler than the gas, the sensor temperature will be less than the gas temperature because of radiant-energy transfer from sensor to wall and because of conductive transfer from sensor through mount to wall. These two energy fluxes from the sensor must be balanced by thermal transfer from the gas to the sensor by the convective and conductive transfer that results from a temperature difference between the gas and the sensor.

The difficulties of temperature measurement of fluids are doubly confounded if very high velocities are involved, so that kinetic-energy effects contribute to the sensor temperature, and if chemical changes, such as dissociations at high temperatures, are occurring in the fluid.

5-14   *Expansion thermometers*

The simplest and most common instrument in this class is the familiar liquid-in-glass thermometer, which can be used solely for indication, not for automatic control or recording.   It is suitable for temperatures as low as −290°F and as high as 1000°F, depending on the choice of thermometric fluid.

For recording and control, the pressure-spring thermometer may be used.   This instrument consists of a *bulb* containing the expansible fluid for the primary sensing, a *capillary tube* to transmit the pressure in the bulb, and a *receiving element*, which is a pressure spring such as a bourbon tube or a helix, to convert the pressure into a motion or displacement. Figure 5-10 shows these features.

The fluid in the bulb usually is a liquid under fairly high pressure, e.g., 400 to 1,200 psi.   A typical bulb size might be 0.5 in. in diameter by 5 in. in length.   Gases, nitrogen usually, may be used as the thermometric fluid, but much larger bulbs are required than for a liquid-filled system, and the response is more sluggish.   Both liquid-filled and gas-filled systems are sensitive to ambient temperatures, especially if the capillary tubing is long.   In some installations the tubing may be as long as 200 ft.

To avoid ambient effects, the vapor-pressure thermometer may be used.   In this thermometer the bulb is half-filled with a pure liquid in equilibrium with its own vapor, which fills the other half of the bulb. As long as the interface between the liquid and gaseous phases is in the bulb, the pressure of the system is an accurate measure of the temperature in the bulb.   The vapor-pressure thermometer has the disadvantages

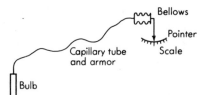

Figure 5-10   Pressure-spring thermometer.

that its scale is nonlinear and it is subject to an aberration in response called the cross-ambient effect. This effect is a sluggishness in response that occurs when the bulb temperature changes sign in respect to the ambient temperature, since the contents of the capillary tube must change phase.

Typical sensing ranges are −100 to 1200°F for liquid-expansion thermometers, −200 to 700°F for gas-expansion thermometers, and −20 to 700°F for vapor-pressure thermometers. The typical minimum range for a single instrument is 100°F. Speed of response is greatest for the vapor-pressure type of instrument; least, for gas expansion.

A variety of simple schemes is available for compensating for ambient effects in the liquid- and gas-expansion thermometers. Compensation for the pressure spring, called case compensation, is effected by the simple expedient of opposing the sensing spring with an identical dead-ended spring. To compensate for the capillary tube as well, the countering spring can be connected to a dead-ended capillary which runs the length of the live capillary.

A third kind of expansion thermometer is the *bimetallic thermometer*, consisting of a helix wound from a strip of two dissimilar materials welded together. One of the materials, for example, the nickel-steel alloy Invar, has a low coefficient of expansion, and the other one, usually brass, has a high coefficient. Changes in temperature cause the bimetallic strip to twist, and the resultant motion of the free end of the helix is a measure of the change in temperature. These thermometers are used frequently for indication, but principally for compensation of other types of thermometers.

5-15   Thermoelectric elements

The most widely used thermometer in the process industries is the thermocouple. Its popularity is due to its simplicity, low cost, swift response, and reliability over virtually the whole range of temperatures of industrial interest.

The thermocouple is a heat engine consisting of two wires of dissimilar materials joined at their ends. If the connections at the two ends are at different temperatures, a current will flow in the circuit commensurate with the net heat exchange at the junctions. A theoretical analysis of the thermoelectric effect may be made by the methods of irreversible thermodynamics, but we do not include such an analysis here.

The effect was discovered by Seebeck in 1821, when he observed that a current flow was produced by a circuit of two different wires with junctions at different temperatures. There are two contributions to the

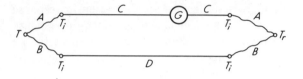

Figure 5-11   Simple thermocouple circuit.

total thermoelectric electromotive force, one from the Peltier effect, due to heat exchange between the junctions and the surroundings, the other from the Thomson effect, due to temperature gradients in the homogeneous wires.

A simple thermocouple circuit is shown in Fig. 5-11.   The wires forming the couple are marked A and B for the two different metals. Inexpensive lead wires C and D, having thermoelectric properties similar to the couple wires, are used for intermediate connections between the hot junction at temperature T and the cold junction (reference junction) at temperature T_r.   In the figure all the intermediate connections are at the same temperature, T_i, including the connections to the galvanometer marked G.

As long as the intermediate points are at the same temperature, the nature of the connecting leads and how many there are have no effect on the net emf in the circuit.   The only pertinent factors are the nature of A and B and the temperature difference $T - T_r$.   This fact can be demonstrated by summing the various voltages around the circuit, namely,

$$E = (E_{BA})_T + (E_A)_{T-T_i} + (E_{AC})_{T_i} + (E_{CA})_{T_i} + (E_A)_{T_i-T_r}$$
$$+ (E_{AB})_{T_r} + (E_B)_{T_r-T_i} + (E_{BD})_{T_i} + (E_{DB})_{T_i} + (E_B)_{T_i-T}$$

or since

$$(E_{AC})_{T_i} = -(E_{CA})_{T_i} \qquad \text{and} \qquad (E_B)_{T_r-T_i} + (E_B)_{T_i-T} = (E_B)_{T_r-T}$$

then

$$E = (E_{BA})_T + (E_A)_{T-T_r} + (E_{AB})_{T_r} + (E_B)_{T_r-T} \tag{5-4}$$

where, for example, $(E_{BA})_T$ is the Peltier emf at the hot junction, and $(E_A)_{T-T_r}$ is the Thomson emf in wire of metal A, with a temperature gradient $T - T_r$.

Industrial thermocouples should be characterized by large thermal emf for easy measurement; by a linear relation between temperature difference and emf for easy recording and easy reference-junction compensation; by resistance to corrosive attack for long life; and by a precise calibration and freedom from drift for standardization and interchangeability.

The four couples in common use, their useful ranges of temperature, and their sensitivity are given in Table 5-1.

Table 5-1   Thermocouple properties

	Practical range, °F	*Sensitivity, mv/°F*
Copper-constantan	−300 to 600	0.033
Iron-constantan	0 to 2200, nonoxidizing atmosphere	0.035
Chromel-alumel	0 to 2500	0.022
Alloys of platinum and rhodium	13 and 10%, and platinum 0 to 3100	0.007

The noble-metal couples resist corrosion and oxidation best, and they are excellently reproducible, but their sensitivity is relatively low. Iron-constantan couples are probably the most widely used.

For increased sensitivity, a number of thermocouples may be connected in series. The resulting element is called a multijunction thermocouple, or a thermopile, and the signal is multiplied by the number of couples so connected. For measuring temperatures to be averaged over a distance, a parallel circuit may be used.

Ordinarily, industrial couples are protected in their installation by metal sleeves called thermowells. The effect of the thermowell may be to change the dynamic character of the sensor from that of a first-order transfer lag, with a time constant as low as 1 sec, to that of a second-order element, with a predominant time constant as much as ten or twenty times greater than that of the couple alone.

Thermocouple outputs are detected by a deflectional instrument (millivoltmeter) or by a balancing instrument (potentiometer). The former is simple and inexpensive, but it is subject to error because it requires that a current flow in the circuit. With the balancing instrument, the system constitutes a null circuit, i.e., no current flow, and consequently, the various resistances in the thermocouple circuit cannot distort the emf generated by the couple.

The balancing circuits can be automatic, self-calibrating, and precisely compensated for fluctuations in the temperature of the cold junction. Figure 5-12 shows a typical balancing circuit. Resistance B is

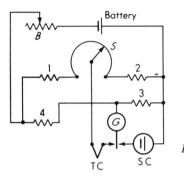

Figure 5-12   Null-balance potentiometer circuit for thermocouple.

used to standardize the battery against the standard cell.   In automatic potentiometers the standardization is carried out by periodic closures of the switch connecting the galvanometer G to the standard cell SC, followed by adjustments to B so that no current flows through the galvanometer.   Resistance 3 limits the current drawn from the standard cell. Resistances 1 and 2 fix the zero and the range of the instrument, and S is the slide-wire resistor, the balance setting of which is the measure of the thermocouple emf.   Resistance 4 is made of wire of temperature-sensitive resistance to compensate for changes in cold-junction temperature.

5-16   Resistance thermometry

This type of thermometry is simple and accurate, and although it is not quite as widely used for industrial measurement and control as the thermocouple, it is popular and its popularity is growing.

The primary sensor in a resistance thermometer is a length of metal wire of total resistance 10 to 100 ohms wound in a compact shape on mica or other nonconductor, or it is a thermistor consisting of a small bead or cylinder of a semiconductor, the resistances of which change appreciably with changes in temperature.   Some typical metals used in resistance thermometers are listed below, with some of their important properties. Nickel is the most common resistance material in industrial instruments.

Table 5-2   *Properties of resistance-thermometer wire*

Metal	$R_{68°F}$, ohms/(mil)(ft)	Upper temperature limit, °F	$R_{100°C}/R_{0°C}$
Platinum	59.1	1200	1.392
Copper	9.4	250	1.431
Nickel	38	600	1.663

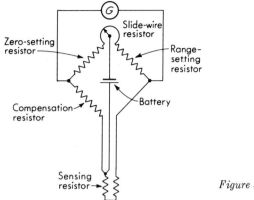

Figure 5-13   Wheatstone-bridge circuit for resistance thermometer.

The last column identifies the relative sensitivities of the different metals expressed as a ratio of resistances at two temperatures.   Although the thermistors are much more sensitive than any of the metals, typically, by a factor of 10 or more, they are subject to drift, and are used more for ambient compensation than for measurement.   Since the sensing element can be very small, 0.1 in. unshielded, for example, the time constant can be as small as 0.1 sec.

Regardless of the type of primary sensor used, the mode of measurement of the resistance most usually involves a bridge circuit similar to the Wheatstone bridge shown in Fig. 5-13.   For industrial instruments the bridge is balanced automatically by a variety of means, depending on the manufacturer.

The approximate range of application of the resistance thermometer is −300 to 1200°F.   In typical industrial uses this thermometer can detect temperature differences as low as 0.03°F.   Because of its accuracy the platinum resistance thermometer defines the International Temperature Scale from −190° to 660°C.

5-17   State of aggregation

The melting points of various solids afford a means of gauging temperatures.   In ceramics manufacture, for example, relatively high temperatures are indicated by the fusion of Seger cones.   Marking crayons are available which indicate the approximate temperature of surfaces when they are rubbed on the surfaces.

Although this class of methods of measuring temperature is important industrially, it is not useful for automatic control.

5-18   Radiation pyrometry

The electromagnetic radiations given off by systems can be measured and used to gauge the temperatures of the systems. Two types of radiation pyrometers are of importance, namely, the total-radiation pyrometer and the optical pyrometer.

The total-radiation pyrometer focuses all the radiant energy it receives onto a sensitive thermometer consisting of a two- to eight-element thermopile or a vacuum thermocouple or a bolometer, which is a resistance element $\frac{1}{2}$ in. long, of 0.1-μ-thick nickel foil coated with platinum black. This pyrometer can be used for temperatures from about 100 to 3200°F.

The optical pyrometer is a partial-radiation pyrometer in that it measures the intensity of radiation at a particular wavelength. It obtains a measure of temperature by comparing the unknown radiation with a calibrated radiation from a controlled source. Since the comparison can be made automatically, this instrument, like the total-radiation pyrometer, can be used for recording and controlling, as well as for indicating. Practical temperature ranges are from 1200 to 5200°F.

Radiation pyrometers are used in processes when the primary sensing element cannot come in direct contact with the material whose temperature is being measured, as, for example, billets in steel-rolling mills, molten metals, and furnaces. The response speeds of these instruments are much greater than those of any other temperature sensors.

5-19   Flow measurement

Flow measurement is probably the oldest art in the field of instrumentation. All flowmeters may be classified as either *quantity* or *inferential meters*. The quantity meters are positive-displacement, or volumetric, meters. They trap or segregate uniform increments of fluid successively and count the increments. Typical examples are the nutating-disk meters used as household water meters; the bellows meters or diaphragm meter used for household and industrial gas meters; the wet-test meter; and the rotary-vane meter.

The quantity meters can be very accurate, but since they do not measure instantaneous flow rates, they are not useful for on-line automatic control.

The inferential meters identify the flow rate from some property related to flow. Among the more important properties for determining flow rate are (1) the pressure drop across a known restriction to the flow,

(2) the impingement force of the flow stream, and (3) various dilutions in the flow stream.

The meters which determine flow rate from the pressure drop across a restriction are by a large margin the most important flowmeters for industrial process control. This class of meters includes (1) the head meter, typical examples of which are the orifice meter, in which the restriction is a round hole in a plate placed normal to the fluid flow, and the venturi meter, in which the restriction is shaped to minimize frictional losses resulting from flow through the restriction; and (2) the area meter, the most commonly used example of which is the rotameter, wherein the position of a float in a tapered tube is indicative of flow rate. Figure 5-14 shows the form of the primary sensors for these meters.

The pressure drop across the orifice, or venturi, tube is measured by the differential-pressure gauges described in Secs. 5-7 to 5-10. The float position in the rotameter usually is transduced to an electric signal when this sensor is used for recording and controlling flows. Unlike the rotameter, the orifice meter involves an inherently nonlinear relation between the measured signal and the flow rate; namely, the flow velocity through the orifice is proportional to the square root of the pressure drop. Differential pressure meters are available which compensate for this nonlinearity, but they are not widely used.

Examples of flowmeters that depend on impingement force are the various propeller meters, the cup anemometer, deflecting-vane anemometer, and the pitot tube. For the first two, speed of rotation is the measure of flow; for the third, it is the force on the vane; and for the pitot tube, it is the pressure equal to the velocity head. Representations of these meters are shown in Fig. 5-15.

Examples of flowmeters that depend on dilution are the Thomas meter and the hot-wire anemometer, both of which relate thermal-energy dissipation to flow velocity. The latter device is particularly useful for measuring local velocities.

Flowmeters generally have quite rapid responses equivalent to slightly damped second-order systems with predominant time constants

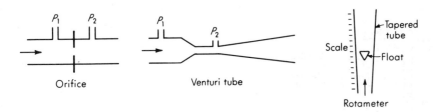

Figure 5-14 Common flowmeter elements, restriction type.

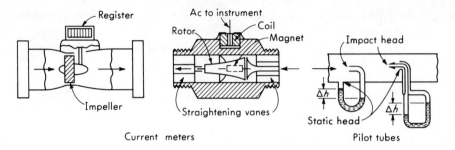

Figure 5-15   Flowmeter elements, impingement-force type.

of about 2 sec or less.   Actually, since flow processes themselves are characterized by very low time constants, the instrumentation associated
with them may contribute significantly to the overall response speed of
the controlled system.

5-20   *Level measurement*

Liquid level is a particularly important process variable, not only
for the maintenance of stable operation, but also for periodic inventory
controls.   It is measured either directly, by means of floats or gauge
glasses, or it is measured indirectly, through the hydrostatic head of the
liquid in the tank.

The instrument of the direct type which is most widely used for
automatic control is the buoyancy displacer, consisting of a small vessel
(displacer) partially immersed at the liquid level (Fig. 5-16).   This
displacer is connected to a pneumatic balance so that the buoyancy
of the displacer produces an air pressure proportional to the level of
immersion.

There are a wide variety of instruments of the hydrostatic type,
including simple bubblers, wherein the gas pressure required to inject a
bubble near the bottom of the tank is a direct measure of the hydrostatic

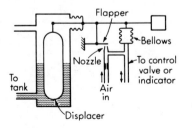

Figure 5-16   Buoyancy-displacement
liquid-level gauge.

head above the nozzle (Fig. 5-17a); differential manometers connected at top and bottom of the tank for tanks under pressure (Fig. 5-17b); and bell and limp diaphragm systems in which the pressure of the gas inside a bell at the bottom of the tank resulting from the motion of a slack diaphragm is a measure of the head above the bell (Fig. 5-17c).

There are a variety of other types of level gauges less widely used than those described above but important for special applications. Among the materials and methods used are radioactive sources plus Geiger counters, capacitance probes, and acoustic techniques.

Since typical liquid-level processes involve large capacitances and correspondingly large time constants, the dynamics of liquid-level gauges ordinarily contribute very little to the overall system dynamics. If the level sensor is mounted in a separate chamber connected to the tank, however, the dynamics can be objectionally sluggish when the connecting lines are improperly sized.

5-21 Composition measurement

It is impractical to attempt a complete cataloging of the methods of measuring the chemical composition of mixtures. The only way to keep abreast of what instruments are available is through the literature of the instrument manufacturers. In the next three sections we review, briefly, the properties which are used as measures of composition for industrial process control.

Many of the process variables we have discussed may be used for composition measurement. The pressure of a two-phase binary system at constant temperatures is one example. Another is the ratio of flow rates of two feed streams into a perfect mixer, which involves a feedforward type of metering.

Composition meters do not lend themselves to easy classification.

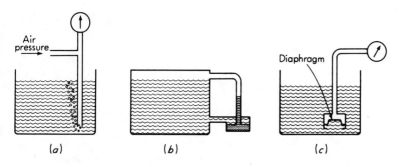

Figure 5-17 Hydrostatic-head liquid-level gauges.

Virtually all of them are based on the measurement of a physical property; relatively few are based on chemistry.

5-22 Spectroscopic methods of composition measurement

Absorption spectrometers determine composition from the extent to which a thin sample of the fluid stream absorbs electromagnetic radiation.   Depending on the wavelengths of the absorption bands used, the instruments are classified as infrared, ultraviolet, and x-ray absorption spectrometers.   In general, the ultraviolet analyzers are less selective but more sensitive than the infrared analyzers.   Any of these instruments may be used for continuous stream analysis of appropriate mixtures, usually mixtures containing a single constituent to be determined.

Emission spectroscopes determine composition from the intensity of radiation from arcs or flames; hence they are particularly suited to metallurgical processes rather than to typical chemical or petroleum processing.

The mass spectrometer identifies the relative amounts of molecules of different masses.   Instruments of narrow ranges of sensitivity are used for continuous gas-stream analysis.   For systems in which a number of constituents must be determined, a concomitant requirement is a high-speed digital computer, to interpret the results.

Spectrometry in the range of radio frequencies includes microwave absorption, electron paramagnetic resonance, and nuclear magnetic resonance.   Of these the last is most widely used industrially.   The basis of use is the tendency of certain element isotopes to absorb energy at radio frequencies when in a magnetic field.

5-23 Methods based on various physical properties

Listed below are some of the more commonly used physical properties for determining fluid compositions and a representative example of the particular methods:

1 *Density* Any of the hydrostatic-head instruments for liquid level become density meters at constant level.

2 *Viscosity* Measure the torque on constant-speed rotor or use paired rotameters, only one of which is sensitive to viscosity.

3 *Electrical conductivity* Use test-cell and bridge circuit.   This method is used more for leak detection than for continuous process control for both gases and liquids.

4 Thermal conductivity Hot-wire cells for gases only. Particularly useful for binary mixtures, provided the components have widely different thermal conductivities.

5 Wet-bulb temperature Use expansion-type or resistance thermometers with wetted bulbs for gauging moisture content of air.

6 Dewpoint Electric hygrometer for determining moisture in gases uses temperature required to establish equilibrium between a hygroscopic conductor and the gas.

7 Magnetic susceptibility For oxygen in gases.

8 Acoustic velocity Measure phase shift of sonic waves to analyze binary mixtures.

9 Index of refraction For transparent binary systems.

10 Dielectric constant For determining polar materials in nonpolar solvents.

11 Gas chromatography Constituents of gas or vapor selectively adsorbed and desorbed in column. Typical sampling lags range from 5 to 30 min, but as many as eight constituents can be determined with high accuracy.

5-24 Chemical methods

1 Orsat analysis Used in furnace combustion control.

2 Combustion Measure temperature rise in calorimeter which catalytically combines any oxygen present with excess hydrogen.

3 Titration Variety of techniques for different materials.

4 pH Use appropriate electrodes and measure emf with balancing potentiometer to measure acidity.

5 Oxidation-reduction potential Similar to pH measurement, but different electrodes for redox reactions.

6 Absorption methods Very specific methods for particular chemicals. Orsat analysis is a special case of multiple successive gas absorption.

7 Gas calorimeter Burn combustible gas at constant rate and measure temperature rise of air coolant.

5-25 Response of composition meters

Clearly, the dynamic characteristics of composition meters will vary quite widely. The range of typical response times is from less than 1 sec to almost 1 hr, and not very useful generalizations are possible.

Often, distance-velocity lags are associated with the sampling of streams for chemical analysis. These lags may occur in the process equipment, for example, when the sampling probe for a reactor must be located in the effluent stream at a significant distance from the reactor. They may also occur in the sensing instrument itself in the transfer of the sample for analysis from the sampler to the analyzer.

In many composition meters the measurement is intermittent because the analyses are conducted batchwise on a fixed schedule. The resulting generation of discrete output signals at fixed intervals of time lends itself to digital-computer manipulation as discussed in Chap. 10. So long as the sampling frequency is much higher than the critical frequencies in the controlled process, the dynamics of the composition meter will not make an objectionable contribution to the overall control system.

5-26   Signal transmission

All measuring and control instruments involve the transmission and the transduction of signals. In some instances, however, signals must be transported over long distances, and special transmitters must be included in the instrumentation to avoid excessive distortion and delay of the signals.

In process instruments the transmission of signals is effected electrically, pneumatically, hydraulically, and mechanically. The last two modes of transmission usually are employed only when the transmission is an integral part of a measuring or controlling instrument. A typical case is the pressure-spring thermometer, wherein the expansion of the thermometric fluid in the primary sensing bulb is transmitted via capillary tubing to the pressure spring over distances as long as 100 ft or more.

Electrical transmission lines are used when all the process instrumentation is electronic or when signals must be transported over distances in excess of about 200 ft. The dynamics of electrical transmission are much too fast to contribute any kind of lag in process control.

Pneumatic transmission lines are usually equipped with amplifying pilots, or boosters. These pilots are very similar in principle to the pneumatic pressure gauge shown in Fig. 5-8.

The dynamics of pneumatic transmission lines may be characterized approximately by a first-order transfer lag with a time constant for a 200-ft length of a little less than $\frac{1}{2}$ sec. At 500 ft the characteristic is a first-order lag of $1\frac{1}{2}$ sec coupled to a pure dead time of $\frac{1}{2}$ sec, the latter arising from the distributed nature of the system parameters.

The responses of hydraulic and mechanical transmitters are faster than those of pneumatic transmitters. Mechanical transmitters, however, may have dead times or discontinuities and, as a consequence, hysteresis effects.

Problems

5-1   Write the transfer function for the pressure gauge in Fig. 5-8, allowing for resistance-capacitance effects and assuming that the outlet pressure is dead-ended in a bellows-pressure element. Show that the ratio of outlet-pressure change to the change in diaphragm position with respect to the nozzle should be large.

5-2   Estimate and sketch the response of a mercury manometer consisting of a steel U tube 0.40 in. ID, with a total mercury-column length of 42 in., when the steady-air-pressure differential across the manometer is increased suddenly from 1 to 4 in. Hg. This manometer is fitted with an adjustable restriction set to give essentially critical damping.

5-3   Write the transfer function of a thermocouple in a high-velocity gas line. The hot junction of the couple is brazed to the inside of the tip of a slender stainless-steel thermowell, 0.120 in. OD, 0.080 in. ID, inserted to a depth of 2 in. in the 4-in.-ID gas line. Under average gas-flow conditions the surface coefficient of heat transfer on the outside of the well is estimated to be 5.0 Btu/(hr)(ft²)(°F). *Data:* Stainless steel: specific gravity, 7.90; thermal conductivity, 16.0 Btu/(hr)(ft²)(°F/ft); specific-heat capacity, 0.15 Btu/(lb)(°F).

5-4   Estimate the static error in the thermometer of Prob. 5-3 if gas-line wall temperature is maintained at an average temperature 40°F below the gas temperature. Assume that the thermocouple radiates energy to the wall at a rate proportional to the temperature difference between the thermowell and the pipe wall and with a rate coefficient based on the outside surface of the thermowell of 2.0 Btu/(hr)(ft²)(°F).

5-5   An anomaly in the performance of liquid-expansion thermometers is the so-called *dip effect*, in which the temperature indication goes the wrong way at the start of the response to step forcing. The dip effect results from the fact that the sensor bulb itself expands when heated. Sketch the form of the step response with the dip effect, and indicate the approximate magnitudes for a mercury-in-steel sensing element in which the volumes of steel and mercury are equal and the effective time constants are 2 sec for the steel wall and 10 sec for the liquid mercury. The coefficients of cubical expansion for steel and mercury are 0.355×10^{-4} and 0.182×10^{-3}, respectively; that is, $v_2 = v_1[1 + C(T_2 - T_1)]$, where C is the coefficient for T in degrees centigrade. Assume that, for the maximum dip effect, the expansion of the volume of steel is reflected entirely in an increase in the enclosed volume.

5-6   A gas flow to a large reactor is metered by a conventional orifice flowmeter. Under normal operating conditions the flowmeter reading oscillates between 10.2 and 10.9 at a constant period of 11 sec. From previous calibrations these two readings correspond to flows of 10,080 and 11,100 cfm at standard conditions of 1 atm pressure and 32°F. What is the integrated average gas-flow rate to the reactor in standard cfm?

5-7 The temperature in a fluidized-bed catalytic reactor is measured by a shielded thermocouple of platinum and platinum containing 12 percent rhodium. Lead wires of copper and a copper-nickel alloy are connected to the couple wires at the head of the thermowell just outside the reactor. Preliminary tests indicate that the thermocouple is giving temperatures which are erroneously high. Estimate the magnitude of error that would result if the lead wires were inadvertently interchanged when the couple was installed. The actual reactor temperature is 850°F, the temperature at the head of the couple thermowell is 205°F, and the reference junction temperature at the potentiometer instrument case is 100°F. Data for Pt 13 percent Rh–Pt thermocouples are:

Temperature, °F	900	850	205	100	32
Emf, mv	4.263	3.969	0.616	0.220	0

controllers and
control action

This chapter is concerned with the characteristics of commercially available process controllers and with the principal types of control action. The power sources for driving controllers are described briefly, and the specific manner in which the various control actions are generated is described for one class of pneumatic controllers.

6-1 Controllers

The typical instrument boxes called *controllers* that we find mounted on the control panels in process plants usually contain a number of different control-loop elements. These elements include a receiving element, a summer, an indicator or recorder, or both, and a control-function generator deployed as shown in the block diagram in Fig. 6-1.

For simple control systems the controller box accepts two signals and produces two signals. Through the receiving element it obtains a measure of the controlled variable $c_2(t)$, and from the reference adjustment it obtains the command signal, or set point, $r(t)$. The summer computes the difference between the set point and the measure of the controlled variable. This difference is the deviation, or error, signal, which is the forcing signal to the control-function generator. The output from the latter is the forcing signal to the final control elements. In addition, the controller has a second output signal in the indication, or record, c_3, of the controlled variable c. These indications, or records, may take many forms, ranging from the position of an index needle on a graduated scale to a numerical printout on sheets of paper.

As an example of what types of signals are involved in a representative controller, consider a typical commercially available pneumatic controller. Usually, the input signal c_1 will be a pressure, and the receiving element will be a pressure spring, as described in Sec. 5-9. The output from the pressure spring is a mechanical displacement which might be used directly to drive not only the index of the indicator or the pen of the recorder, but also the lever for the summer. If the summer consists of a system of levers, the set-point adjustment will also involve the mechanical positioning of a lever. The deviation signal then will be another mechanical displacement which alters the resistance to air flows in the system of resistances and capacitances constituting the control-function generator. The final output m, the manipulated variable, will be an air pressure.

6-2   Controller power sources

Controllers may be classified by the chief source of power used, as, for example, electric, pneumatic, mechanical, and hydraulic controllers.

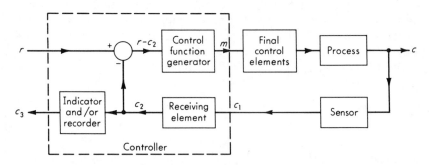

Figure 6-1 Typical elements in process controller.

All four of these classes have response speeds in their control actions well beyond the requirements of most normal processes. In years past, pneumatic controls invariably were specified for locations such as organic chemicals plants and petroleum refineries where potential fire hazards existed. In recent years, electric controls and instrumentation have been used increasingly in these locations because of safer designs of the instruments.

Electric and pneumatic controls are roughly competitive. The easy transmission and manipulation of electric signals is offset by the fact that pneumatic actuators for valves are much cheaper than electric actuators. In applications where the instrumentation is coupled to computers or other electrical data processors, the advantages may lie with electric controllers.

6-3 *Discontinuous control; two-position control*

All types of control action can be classified broadly into two categories: discontinuous control and continuous control. The discontinuous-control mode may be subdivided further into two-position and multiple-position control.

In ideal two-position control the controller output depends on the sign of the deviation, and not on its magnitude. Thus, for the control-function generator shown in Fig. 6-2, if the full-range output is 0 to 100 percent, the relationship between forcing and response is

$$m = \begin{cases} 0\% & \text{for } \theta_r - \theta_c < 0 \\ 100\% & \text{for } \theta_r - \theta_c > 0 \end{cases} \tag{6-1}$$

This kind of control is also called *bang-bang* control and *on-off* control, and the mechanism for generating the action is a simple relay.

In actual practice, it is not possible to build a device that is sensitive to the sign of extremely small deviations, nor is it desirable to do so. The excessively sensitive controller would undergo needless wear and tear on its moving parts and contacts. What is done with commercial two-position controllers is to provide them with a *dead zone* of from 0.5 to 2.0 percent of full range straddling the set point. No control action takes place when the controlled variable lies within the dead zone, or *differential gap*, or neutral zone, as it is sometimes called. Figure 6-3 shows the effect of the dead zone on the response of an on-off controller to sinusoidal forcing in the controlled variable. The width of the neutral zone designated by the dashed lines is exaggerated in the figure for clarity.

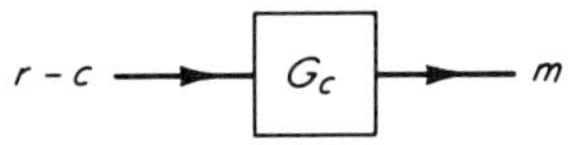

$r - c \longrightarrow \boxed{G_c} \longrightarrow m$

Figure 6-2 Control-function generator.

Note that the effect of the neutral zone, or dead zone, is to increase the phase lag of the response. With no gap the controller output is exactly 180° out of phase with the controlled variable, but with increasing gap the phase lag increases to a maximum of 270°. Note also that the response is not a perfectly rectangular wave. The slopes of the sides of the rectangles in this case identify the finite rates of going from one extremum of output to the other. These slopes would be flatter if the final control elements, including the actuator and the valve, were included in the response. In process systems where the on-off controlling element is an electric relay, as in some industrial furnace controls, for example, the side slopes of the controller response are effectively infinite.

Two-position control, in particular, on-off control, is the most widely used type of control action. The instruments used for this kind of control are cheap, rugged, and virtually foolproof. For systems characterized by large capacitances and subjected to small disturbances, two-position control provides excellent economical control. Household heating systems, constant-temperature baths, and level controls in large inventory systems are typical of the systems for which on-off controllers are most effective.

On-off control is inherently oscillatory in character, but for large-capacitance systems, the amplitude of oscillation of the controlled variable can be quite small. In household heating systems, for example, the actual excursions of the room temperatures ordinarily are undetectable on household thermometers.

For systems like typical fluid-flow systems which have very low capacitances, on-off control alone would be disastrous.

6-4 Multiple-position control

A variant of two-position control with differential gap is three-position control wherein the controller responds with an intermediate

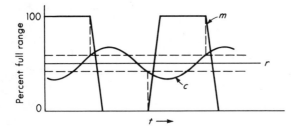

Figure 6-3 On-off control with dead zone.

output when the controlled variable lies within the neutral zone.   Figure 6-4 illustrates the kind of response produced by this type of control.

Three-position control offers essentially the same advantages as two-position control, with the additional advantage of decreased tendencies toward oscillation.

Commercial controllers with as many as three intermediate output positions, effectively five-position control, are available but not widely used.

6-5 *Proportional control*

The basic continuous-control mode is *proportional control*, in which the controller output is proportional to the deviation, namely,

$$\frac{m}{r - c} = K_P \qquad\qquad (6\text{-}2)$$

where K_P is the proportional gain, and the m, r, and c are perturbations about normal operating levels.

Equation (6-2) may be written

$$m = K_P(r - c)$$

which, transformed term by term, is

$$M = K_P(R - C)$$

and the transfer function for the proportional-control-function generator is

$$G_c = \frac{M}{R - C} = K_P \qquad\qquad (6\text{-}3)$$

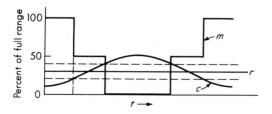

Figure 6-4   Three-position control.

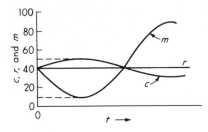

Figure 6-5   Proportional control.

If we hold the reference input constant and let

$$c = A \sin \omega t \qquad (6\text{-}4)$$

we find

$$m = -K_P A \sin \omega t = K_P A \sin (\omega t - \pi) \qquad (6\text{-}5)$$

These equations are plotted in Fig. 6-5 for respective normal operating levels of $c = r = 40$ and $m = 50$ and for $K_P = 4.0$ and $A = 10$.

From Eqs. (6-4) and (6-5) the frequency-response characteristics for the ratio M/C are a constant magnitude ratio of K_P and a constant phase angle of $-180°$ or a phase lag of $180°$. The frequency-response characteristics for the control-function generator alone, namely, $M/(R - C)$, are a magnitude ratio of K_P and a phase angle of zero. These latter characteristics are shown in a Bode plot in Fig. 6-6 for $K_P = 10$. The drop in both magnitude ratio and phase at very high frequencies is typical of real systems. Usually, these frequencies are much higher than the frequencies which are pertinent for process control. In pneumatic controllers, for example, these frequencies are of the order of 1 cycle/sec.

The frequency-response characteristics for the control-function generator plus the summer in Fig. 6-7 are shown on a Nyquist diagram in

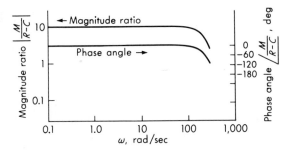

Figure 6-6   Bode diagram for proportional control,
$K_P = 10$.

Fig. 6-8.   The vector locus is a single point on the real axis at $-K_P$ for all frequencies up to the point where the magnitude and phase begin falling off.

Although proportional control is the basic continuous-control mode, the fact that its action produces a particular output for a particular deviation results in a serious disadvantage.   Proportional control will tolerate a steady-state error.   A detailed treatment of this property of proportional control is given in Chap. 8, but a qualitative appraisal can be given here.

Consider a heat exchanger under proportional control in which a flowing oil stream is heated to some desired temperature by means of steam condensing outside of the tubes carrying the oil.   At steady conditions of balance at some particular oil-flow rate and oil-inlet temperature, the controller output for zero deviation will provide the proper steam flow to make the oil-outlet temperature equal to·the desired set-point temperature.   Now, if the load on the exchanger changes, as would be the case if the oil-flow rate or the oil-inlet temperature changed, the steam flow would have to change to accommodate the new load.   With proportional control alone, the only way the steam flow can be changed is by changing the deviation from zero to some finite steady-state error, or *offset,* and a new condition of balance can be maintained only if this offset is sustained.

The steady-state error will be small if the proportional gain is high. Commercial controllers with high gains, typically adjustable from 10 to about 50, are called *narrowband proportional controllers.*   This name arises from the fact that the controller gain parameter is frequently designated as *percent proportional band,* defined by

$$PB = \frac{100}{K_P} \tag{6-6}$$

where PB is percent proportional band.   Thus, for narrowband proportional controllers, the proportional-band range is from 2 to 10 percent.

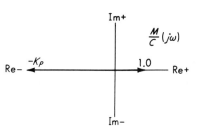

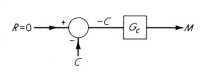

Figure 6-7   Control-function genera-   *Figure 6-8*   Nyquist diagram for pro-
tor plus summer.   portional control.

Broadband proportional controllers have adjustable proportional bands from 10 to above 100 percent, but this control action is always coupled to other actions, as described in subsequent sections.

The proportional band may be regarded as the travel in the controlled variable at constant reference required to produce a 100 percent change in controller output.

In the limit of maximum gain, the narrowband controller approximates on-off control.

6-6   *Integrating action*

Integrating action, or integral control action, produces an output which is proportional to the time integral of the deviation, namely,

$$m = \frac{1}{T_I} \int (r - c) \, dt \tag{6-7}$$

where T_I is the *integral time*.

By differentiating this equation, we find that the rate of change of the controller output is proportional to the deviation. Thus

$$\frac{dm}{dt} = \frac{1}{T_I} (r - c) \tag{6-8}$$

The response to step forcing may be obtained from the transfer function for this kind of control, which function, by transforming Eq. (6-7), is

$$G_c = \frac{M}{R - C} = \frac{1}{T_I s} \tag{6-9}$$

If r is increased suddenly from its initial steady condition by an amount A, $R - C = A/s$, and therefore, from Table 3-1,

$$m = L^{-1} \left[\frac{A}{T_I s^2} \right] = \frac{A}{T_I} t \tag{6-10}$$

This response is a ramp function, as shown in Fig. 6-9. The same response would result from a sudden decrease of c to $-A$.

By substituting $j\omega$ for s in Eq. (6-9), we find

$$\frac{M}{R - C} (j\omega) = \frac{1}{j\omega T_I} = -j \frac{1}{\omega T_I} \tag{6-11}$$

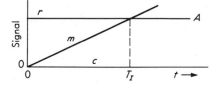

Figure 6-9   Step response of integral controller.

and the frequency-response characteristics therefore are the magnitude ratio

$$\text{MR} = \left| \frac{M}{R - C} (j\omega) \right| = (\text{Im}^2 + \text{Re}^2)^{\frac{1}{2}} = \frac{1}{\omega T_I} \tag{6-12}$$

and the phase angle

$$\psi = \tan^{-1} \frac{\text{Im}}{\text{Re}} = \tan^{-1} (-\infty) = -90° \tag{6-13}$$

The inverse characteristics are

$$\left| \frac{R - C}{M} (j\omega) \right| = \omega T_I \tag{6-14}$$

and

$$\psi = \tan^{-1} (+\infty) = +90° \tag{6-15}$$

These characteristics are shown in Nyquist diagrams with and without the summer in Fig. 6-10 and in a Bode diagram in Fig. 6-11.

Note on the Bode diagram that the magnitude ratio falls off at a slope of -1, and at a frequency of $1/T_I$ rad/unit time it is unity. At zero frequency the integrating action produces infinite gain. As is shown in Chap. 8, this characteristic makes integral control effective in preventing steady-state error.

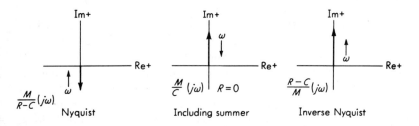

Figure 6-10   Nyquist diagrams for integral control.

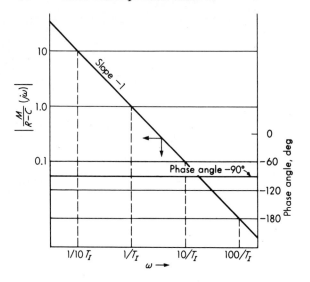

Figure 6-11   Bode diagram for integral control.

The output from integral control is always changing as long as there is a deviation.   As a consequence, integral control is sometimes called *proportional-speed floating control*, since the output is floating, not fixed, and the speed at which it changes is proportional to the deviation.   A variant of this control is *constant-speed floating control*, in which the output is always changing at constant rate.   This characteristic may be achieved in a practical way by coupling on-off control to a valve driven by a constant but relatively low speed motor.

Integral control is not often used entirely alone, although it is effective for low-capacitance systems subjected to large load changes, as in the case of many flow-control systems.   More frequently, it is coupled to proportional control to eliminate the possibility of offset in systems where the stable characteristic of proportional control is necessary.

6-7   *Proportional plus integral control* $(P + I)$

The steady-state error that is possible with systems controlled by the proportional-control mode alone may be eliminated by adjusting the set point of the controller to whatever value is required to balance the controlled variable at the desired value.   This procedure is a *manual resetting* of the controller reference to ensure accurate control.   The same effect can be obtained continuously and automatically by adding integrating action to the proportional action; the result is called proportional control with *automatic reset*.

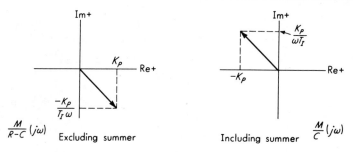

$\frac{M}{R-C}(j\omega)$ Excluding summer   Including summer $\frac{M}{C}(j\omega)$

Figure 6-12   Nyquist diagrams for proportional plus integral control.

The controller transfer function for proportional plus integral control is

$$\frac{M}{R-C} = K_P \left(1 + \frac{1}{T_I s} \right) \tag{6-16}$$

where K_P is the proportional gain as before, but the effective coefficient on the integrating term is K_P/T_I. Some instrument manufacturers calibrate the integral-control adjustment in *repeats per minute*, $1/T_I$, since this factor, the reset rate, identifies the number of times per minute that the integrating action duplicates the proportional-control action.

The frequency-response characteristics of this type of control are shown in Figs. 6-12 and 6-13 for particular values of the controller parameters K_P and T_I and, in the case of Fig. 6-12, only one frequency.

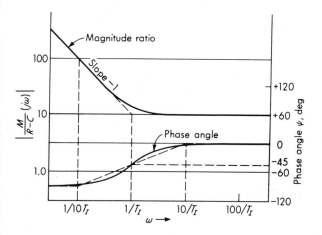

Figure 6-13   Bode diagram for proportional plus integral control.

In Fig. 6-12 the right-hand Nyquist diagram includes the summer in the controller, and therefore the response vector lies 180° out of phase with the response vector for the control-function generator alone. The vector loci for all frequencies are vertical straight lines. If the summer is included, the locus lies in the second quadrant and terminates for infinite frequency at $-K_P$. If the summer is excluded, the vector locus lies in the fourth quadrant and terminates at $+K_P$.

The Bode diagram (Fig. 6-13) has a break frequency at $1/T_I$. At this frequency the straight-line asymptotes for the magnitude ratio intersect at the proportional gain K_P, in this case approximately 10, and the phase angle is exactly $-45°$.

6-8   *Proportional plus derivative control* $(P + D)$

Derivative action generates a controller output which is proportional to the rate of change of the deviation. Thus

$$m = T_D \frac{d(r - c)}{dt} \tag{6-17}$$

where T_D is the derivative time.

This action by itself cannot control anything since its effect is to resist changes in any direction regardless of the magnitude of the error. However, when coupled to proportional-control action, the derivative action can often increase the stability of the control system. The dynamic equation for this control combination, expressed as the transfer

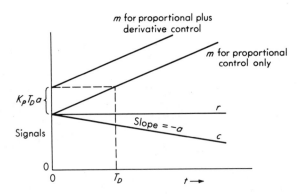

Figure 6-14   Lead time with derivative action.

function, is

$$\frac{M}{R - C} = K_P(1 + T_D s) \tag{6-18}$$

Some instrument manufacturers call T_D the *rate time*, or *lead time*, because this time is the interval by which the derivative action leads, or anticipates, the action resulting from proportional control alone. This property may be visualized readily from Fig. 6-14, which shows the responses of proportional control and of proportional plus derivative control when the controlled variable changes at constant rate. At zero time, c is allowed to fall off at a constant rate a. The derivative action immediately applies a constant corrective increment of $K_P T_D a$, and the proportional action produces a changing correction equal to $K_P a t$. Clearly, the proportional action alone will take T_D units of time to produce the same output that the derivative action produces initially.

The frequency-response characteristics for proportional plus derivative control are shown in Fig. 6-15 for the controller output response to sinusoidal forcing in the controlled variable at a single frequency and in Fig. 6-16 for the control-function generator alone for a wide range of frequencies. In the Nyquist diagram the vector locus for the controller, including the summer, is a vertical straight line beginning at $-K_P$ and extending into the third quadrant.

6-9 Three-mode control

The effect of derivative action ordinarily is to stabilize the control system, and hence permit increasing the controller sensitivity, and consequently increasing the speed of response. For systems where it is desirable to speed the response and at the same time eliminate steady-state error, it is advantageous to use three-mode control, which is the combination of proportional, integral, and derivative control actions $(P + I + D)$.

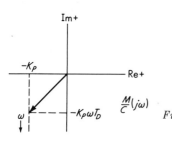

Figure 6-15 Nyquist diagram for proportional plus derivative control.

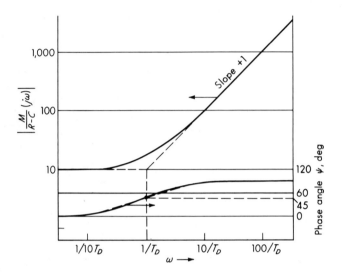

Figure 6-16 Bode diagram for proportional plus derivative control.

For ideal three-mode control, the individual control actions are additive, and the controller transfer function is given by

$$G_c = \frac{M}{R - C} = K_P \left(1 + \frac{1}{T_I s} + T_D s \right) \tag{6-19}$$

A Nyquist diagram for ideal three-mode control at one frequency is shown in Fig. 6-17 for the function M/C.   Again, the vector locus for all possible frequencies is a vertical straight line through $-K_P$, this time extending infinitely into the second and third quadrants.

In the Bode diagram for ideal three-mode control shown in Fig. 6-18, there are two break frequencies.   The control gain is infinite at zero fre-

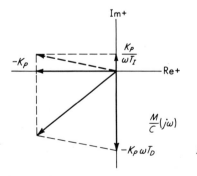

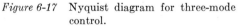

Figure 6-17 Nyquist diagram for three-mode control.

quency and at infinite frequency, and at these limits the phase angle is −90 and +90°, respectively. Thus the integrating action makes its contribution at low frequencies, and the derivative action makes its contribution at high frequencies.

6-10 Compensated rate action

Most commercially available controllers generate control actions which, in respect to proportional action, integral action, or combinations of these two actions, behave ideally as described by the equations in previous sections. The addition of derivative action, however, ordinarily is not made in the manner prescribed by Eq. (6-19), because the high gain that the ideal derivative action produces at high frequency may make the controller unduly sensitive to noise or other high-frequency disturbances. For example, the effect of step forcing in the response signal to a controller which had ideal derivative action would be to saturate the control action. A positive step is an infinitely positive rate of change in the input signal to the control-function generator, and the resulting control action would be zero output. Similarly, a negative step would result in full controller output.

As a result of this excessive sensitivity, the gain at high frequencies usually is limited in commercial instruments which incorporate derivative

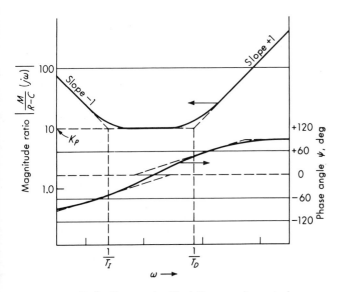

Figure 6-18 Bode diagram for ideal three-mode control.

action, and this limited derivative action is called *compensated rate action*. It is produced by adding an integration which overrides the derivative action at some high frequency in accordance with the transfer function in Eq. (6-20) for proportional plus compensated rate control.

$$G_c = K_P \frac{1 + T_D s}{1 + a T_D s} \tag{6-20}$$

In this equation, a is a constant ranging from about 0.05 to about 0.1, depending on the instrument manufacturer.

The frequency-response characteristics corresponding to Eq. (6-20) are shown in Fig. 6-19. Dashed lines in the figure are the straight-line asymptotic approximations used in constructing the characteristics.

A three-mode controller with the same kind of limitation on the derivative action would have the transfer function

$$G_c = K_P \left(1 + \frac{1}{T_I s}\right) \frac{1 + T_D s}{1 + a T_D s}$$

which may be written

$$G_c = K_P \frac{1 + T_I s}{T_I s} \frac{1 + T_D s}{1 + a T_D s} \tag{6-21}$$

The frequency-response characteristics for this controller are shown in Fig. 6-20, again with the approximation used for the construction indicated by dashed lines.

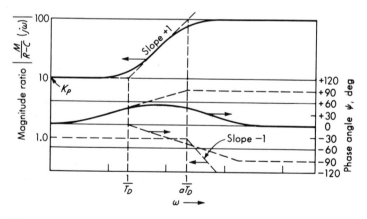

Figure 6-19 Bode diagram for proportional plus compensated rate control.

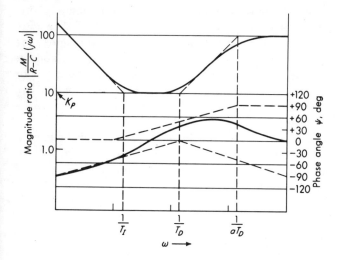

Figure 6-20 Bode diagram for three-mode control with compensated rate action.

6-11 *Pneumatic control-function generation* $(P + I)$

Although the particular manner in which a controller produces its output signals is of no direct consequence to the designer of process control systems, it is instructive to see how a few simple building blocks can be used to generate all the principal control actions.

Figure 6-21 shows a simple assembly consisting of (1) a flapper connected to an adjustable pivot point, (2) a nozzle through which there is a continual small air leak, (3) two opposed bellows thrusting against the flapper, and (4) two airflow restrictions.

Clean dry supply air, typically at 20 psig, enters the system through a fixed restriction, which has the purpose of limiting the airflow so that the full range of output pressures, m, for the extreme positions of the flapper in respect to the nozzle will be 3 to 15 psig. At intermediate

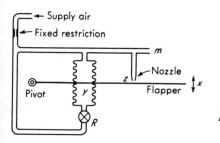

Figure 6-21 Pneumatic proportional plus integral action.

positions of the flapper the output pressure will be approximately proportionate to the flapper position. As was shown in Sec. 5-10, the addition of a negative-feedback bellows, the topside bellows in the figure, can ensure a nearly exact proportionality between the forcing signal x and the response m, provided the amplification in signal z to give m is very large. For typical pneumatic controllers, flapper displacements of only 0.001 to 0.002 in. suffice to produce the full 12-psi range of output pressures, corresponding to an amplification of 6,000 to 12,000 psi/in.

In order to add integrating action, a positive-feedback bellows is set in opposition to the negative-feedback bellows. If the two bellows are of the same size and have the same spring characteristics, the net flapper position z will be given by

$$z = k_1 x + k_2 y - k_2 m \tag{6-22}$$

where $x = r - c$, the deviation
$\quad\quad y =$ pressure in lower bellows
$\quad\quad m =$ pressure in upper bellows and at controller output
$\quad\quad k_1, k_2 =$ dimensional or proportionality constants (steady-state gains)

Since z is very nearly zero because of the large gain in the flapper-nozzle combination, we may rewrite Eq. (6-22) as

$$m - y = \frac{k_1}{k_2} x$$

which, by Laplace transformation, becomes

$$M - Y = \frac{k_1}{k_2} X \tag{6-23}$$

The integrating bellows under the flapper and its adjustable restriction R constitute a simple first-order transfer stage with an effective time constant T_I equal to the product of the pneumatic resistance R and the effective capacitance of the bellows. Thus

$$\frac{Y}{M} = \frac{1}{1 + T_I s} \tag{6-24}$$

By substituting Eq. (6-24) in Eq. (6-23) and rearranging the result, we find that the transfer function for this system is identically that for proportional plus integral control, namely,

$$\frac{M}{X} = K_P \left(1 + \frac{1}{T_I s} \right) \tag{6-25}$$

where $K_P = k_1/k_2$.

Since the pivot position on the flapper is adjustable, k_1, and hence K_P, can be adjusted. The reset rate for the integrating action is adjusted by changing the small needle valve, which is the resistance R.

6-12 *Pneumatic three-mode control* $(P + I + D)$

The addition of derivative action to a pneumatic proportional controller of the flapper-nozzle type is effected by interposing an adjustable restriction in the air line between the negative-feedback bellows and the nozzle. This addition is shown in Fig. 6-22 for the proportional plus integral controller of Fig. 6-21.

Now the net flapper position z is given by

$$z = k_1 x + k_2 y_1 - k_2 y_2 \tag{6-26}$$

where y_1 is the pressure in the integrating bellows and y_2 is the pressure in the proportional, or negative-feedback, bellows.

Again, neglecting z and transforming the remaining terms gives

$$Y_2 - Y_1 = \frac{k_1}{k_2} X = K_P X \tag{6-27}$$

The transfer function for the integrating bellows plus resistance R_1 is

$$\frac{Y_1}{Y_2} = \frac{1}{1 + T_I s} \tag{6-28}$$

and similarly, for the proportioning bellows plus the derivative resistance R_2, it is

$$\frac{Y_s}{M} = \frac{1}{1 + T_D s} \tag{6-29}$$

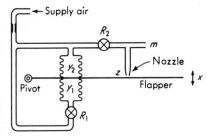

Figure 6-22 Pneumatic three-mode control $(P + I + D)$.

where T_D is the product of the resistance R_2 and the effective capacitance of the negative-feedback bellows.

By eliminating Y_2 and Y_1 from Eqs. (6-27) to (6-29) and solving for the controller transfer function, we obtain

$$\frac{M}{X} = K_P \frac{(1 + T_I s)(1 + T_D s)}{T_I s}$$

or

$$\frac{M}{X} = K_P \left[\left(1 + \frac{T_D}{T_I}\right) + \frac{1}{T_I s} + T_D s \right] \tag{6-30}$$

The three terms within the brackets contribute, respectively, the proportional action, the integral action, and the derivative action. For this system the proportional gain is $K_P(1 + T_D/T_I)$, and hence it is not possible to adjust the gain independently by shifting only the flapper-pivot position.

We have chosen to illustrate the generation of control actions through the use of pneumatic devices involving flapper-nozzle combinations for producing high integral gains. Modern pneumatic controllers employ a variety of precise valving and nozzle-baffle devices, and in compact instruments the pneumatic circuitry affords less convenient illustration than the simple systems we have examined. In all pneumatic systems generating the conventional control modes, however, a central characteristic is the fact that an infinitesimal displacement produces the full output range of the controller.

The generation of the conventional control actions, proportional, integral, and derivative, by hydraulic and electric controllers, follows principles similar to those discussed above.

6-13   *Other control modes*

There is no reason in principle why we cannot use control modes involving successive integrations or differentiations of the deviation beyond those described in the preceding sections. As a practical matter for process control systems, however, there is no advantage, and often there is a serious disadvantage. Higher-order differentiating action, for example, is acutely sensitive to modest excursions of the controlled variable or the set point.

Multiple integrations have been found to be useful for special flow control systems, as, for example, in blowdown-tank wind-tunnel systems, where rapid manipulation of large valves is required to maintain constant flow velocities in a test section, despite rapidly changing pressures before and after the section.

For chemical process systems, however, the normal direction for increased complexity of control action does not lie in increased integrations or differentiations of error signals, but rather in the elaboration of computation of the forcing signal to the controller. A simple example is the control of a gas flow. The typical instruments for flow measurement actually measure flow velocity, whereas the property important in process control may be the mass flow rate. By measuring the density or the temperature and pressure of the process fluid as well as the flow velocity, the actual mass flow rate can be computed, and this computation can be done simply and economically by small analog elements associated with the controller. There are a variety of other simple computations of this sort which can be done without elaborate equipment but which can contribute significantly to improved process control. These computations appear to offer greater advantages in automatic process control than do arbitrary elaborations of the conventional control modes.

Some of these possibilities are examined in Chap. 10.

Problems

6-1 Sketch the frequency-response characteristics on a Bode diagram for an ideal three-mode controller for which the proportional band is 60 percent, the reset rate is 20 repeats per minute, and the lead time is 1 min.

6-2 Repeat Prob. 6-1 for the case where the derivative action is compensated by an integrating component with a break frequency fifteen times the break frequency for the derivative contribution.

6-3 Prove that the system of Fig. 6-21 in the absence of the integrating bellows and restriction will generate proportional-control action.

6-4 Sketch the response of a proportional plus integral controller to a sinusoidal change of 20 percent amplitude and 1-min period in the controlled variable when the proportional band is set at 120 percent and the reset rate is 40 repeats per minute. The reference signal is steady at 50 percent; the controlled variable initially is at 50 percent; the sinusoidal change begins with positive slope; and the controller output is initially 8 psig in a full range of 3.0 to 15.0 psig.

6-5 Repeat Prob. 6-4 for the case where the controlled variable is initially at 40 percent.

6-6 Sketch the signal-flow diagram for the system of Fig. 6-21.

6-7 Sketch the signal-flow diagram for the system of Fig. 6-22.

6-8 Repeat Prob. 6-4 for a proportional plus derivative controller set to 20 percent proportional band and a lead time of 6 min.

6-9 Repeat Prob. 6-8 for the case where the proportional band is set at 12 percent.

6-10 Identify the characteristics of a proportional plus inverse derivative controller for which the transfer function is

$$G_c = \frac{K_P(1 + 10T_D s)}{1 + T_D s}$$

where T_D may be set to values of from 1 to 10 min, and K_P from 1 to 40.

final control
elements

In automatic control systems the output from the controller goes to the final control elements. For most process systems these final control elements are valves and their driving motors. The various types of valves and valve actuators are reviewed in this chapter, and their dynamic characteristics are related to typical process characteristics. Actuators are classified on the basis of their source of power; valves, on the basis of style and lift-flow characteristics.

7-1 Pneumatic actuators

The most commonly used valve motors, or actuators, in the process industries are those which are driven pneumatically.   Figure 7-1 shows a diagram of the principal example of this class of actuators, the diaphragm motor.

The diaphragm is spring-loaded in opposition to the driving air pressure, so that the valve-stem position is proportional to the air pressure.   Usually, the diaphragm is limp type, made of rubber fabric or other resistant material, and supported by a backup plate.

With diaphragm motors, the maximum available *stroke*, or travel, of the valve stem is typically 2 to 3 in.   For longer strokes the valve actuator may be a double-acting piston, or it may be a rotary pneumatic motor driving a rack or a worm gear.   These actuators are capable of driving very large valves, with strokes in the case of the rotary motor up to 5 ft.

7-2 Valve positioner

There is no guarantee that the application of a particular air pressure to the diaphragm of the valve motor in Fig. 7-1 will produce a particular position of the valve stem.   Indeed, if the valve stem is frozen in its seal or stuffing box, it may not move at all, or it may move quite sluggishly.   To avoid this difficulty, the valve motor may be provided with a servomechanism which supplies sufficient pressure through a pilot amplifier to the diaphragm to ensure that the valve stem attains the desired position.   This kind of actuator is called a valve positioner, and usually it requires a source of higher-pressure air, for example, 100 psig, than the normal instrument air (20 psig).   A schematic diagram of a diaphragm motor valve with positioner is shown in Fig. 7-2.

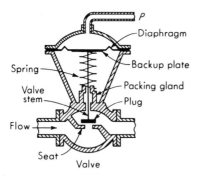

Figure 7-1   Diaphragm motor valve (DMV).

Both the piston-type pneumatic actuator and the rotary pneumatic motor are equipped with built-in valve positioners so that valve-stem position is assuredly proportional to the input air signal.

7-3   *Hydraulic actuators*

The forcing signal to hydraulic actuators is either a mechanical displacement or a pneumatic or electric signal which is transduced to a mechanical displacement.   In the piston-type hydraulic actuator this displacement positions the cylinder valves, which admit oil to either side of the piston, thereby positioning the piston shaft which drives the valve stem.

In the variable-delivery pump type of hydraulic actuator, the input displacement fixes the stroke of a number of piston pumps connected in parallel.   The output-oil delivery of these pumps, which is proportional to the forcing displacement, is fed to a positive-displacement motor to generate an output displacement which is also proportional to the original forcing displacement.   The variable output of the piston pumps also can be fed to the positive-displacement motor in such a manner that the rate of travel of the output displacement is proportional to the input displacement, with the result that the actuator generates an integrating action.

Hydraulic actuators are used where high speeds and large forces are required.

7-4   *Electric actuators*

Electric actuators usually are reversing motors driven by a circuit appropriate to the forcing signal.   They tend to be slower than the pneumatic and hydraulic actuators and more costly for the same performance by a factor of from 2 to 10.   For the special case of on-off, or two-position, control, the spring-loaded solenoid is widely used.   It is inexpensive, and its response can be very fast.

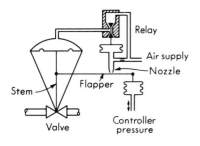

Figure 7-2   Diaphragm   motor   valve   with positioner.

One of the major deterrents to the use of entirely electric control systems is the high cost and relatively poor performance of electric actuators. At the present time the common practice in systems involving electric controllers is to use electropneumatic actuators in which a pilot transducer converts the electric signal to an air pressure, which in turn drives a diaphragm motor.

7-5   Sliding-stem control valves

Control valves may be classified as sliding-stem valves, pinch valves, and rotary-shaft valves. The sliding-stem valves are like the valve in Fig. 7-1 in that the plug is positioned by the stem, which slides through a packing gland. These valves may have single-seated plugs as in Fig. 7-1 or double-seated plugs as in Fig. 7-3a, or they may be gate valves as in Fig. 7-3b.

The single-seated plug valve has the advantage that it can be shut off to give zero flow, but large forces may be required to move the valve stem because of the pressure drop across the opening, or port, between the plug and the seat. Double-seated plug valves avoid the difficulty of large forces on the stem by having the forces at the two plugs in opposition, with the result that only modest forces are required to position the stem.

A variety of plug types is available. Some of the more important ones are shown in Fig. 7-4. The V-port plugs are hollow cylinders, with inverted V notches through which the fluid flows. As the stem rises, more notch area is exposed and the flow increases. The two equal-percentage plugs are shaped to give a particular lift-flow characteristic, as described in Sec. 7-8.

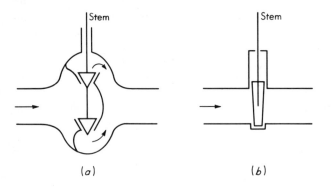

Figure 7-3 Sliding-stem valves.   (a) Double-seat plug valve; (b) gate valve.

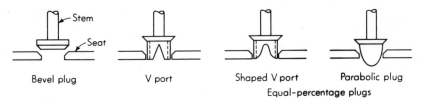

Bevel plug   V port   Shaped V port   Parabolic plug

Equal-percentage plugs

Figure 7-4   Plug types.

Gate valves are advantageous in controlling the flow of fluids containing solid material because there is little change in flow direction within the valve, and consequently little opportunity for the solids to deposit out and cause blockages.

7-6   *Pinch valves*

Two examples of pinch valves are shown in Fig. 7-5.   An important form of the weir valve is the Saunders patent valve.   Both the weir and the hose valves are used for corrosive liquids or slurries where there might be difficulty in maintaining the packing gland with sliding-stem valves. The diaphragm and the hose, which seal in the process fluids, can be made of a wide variety of flexible and corrosion-resistant materials.

7-7   *Rotary shaft valves*

The three principal types of rotating shaft valves are shown in Fig. 7-6.   In the rotary plug valve, the plug is a close-fitting tapered cylinder. Rotation of the stem alters the alignment of ports in the plug with the flow entry and exit of the valve.   Any desired flow characteristic can be obtained with this valve by modifying the shape of the ports in the plug. Furthermore, a total shutoff is possible.

The butterfly valve consists of a duct or body of circular or rectan-

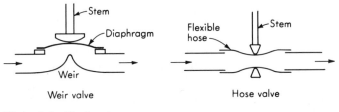

Weir valve   Hose valve

Figure 7-5   Pinch valves.

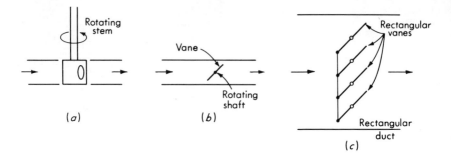

Figure 7-6 Rotary shaft valves. (*a*) Rotary plug valve; (*b*) butterfly valve;
(*c*) louver.

gular cross section containing a flat plate, or vane, slightly smaller than
the duct cross section. Rotation of the vane about a shaft extending
through the duct wall permits an adjustment of flows from nearly zero,
when the vane is normal to the flow, to a maximum flow nearly equal to
the maximum that could be passed through the empty duct.

The louver consists of a series of rectangular vanes connected so
that they rotate together and mounted inside a large rectangular duct.
Both the butterfly valve and the louver are used for gases, although in
some cases the former may be used for liquids and, in special designs, is
capable of total shutoff.

7-8 *Control-valve characteristics*

Control valves are characterized by their rangeability, turndown,
and flow-lift behavior.

Rangeability is the ratio of the maximum controllable flow through
the valve to the minimum controllable flow. Normally, control valves
do not close off entirely lest the valve seats be damaged or the valves stick.
The flow in the normally closed position ranges from about 2 to 4 percent
of the maximum flow, depending on the kind of valve and its size. These
percentages correspond to rangeabilities of 50 to 25. For sliding-stem
control valves the rangeabilities typically lie between 20 and 70.

Turndown is the ratio of the normal maximum flow through the
valve to the minimum controllable flow. Since a practical rule of thumb
is that a control valve should be sized so that the maximum flow under
operating conditions is approximately 70 percent of the maximum possible
flow, the turndown ordinarily is about 70 percent of the rangeability.

The flow through a control valve depends not only on the extent to
which the valve is open, that is, on the *lift*, but also on the pressure drop

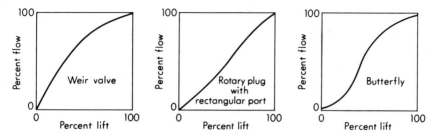

Figure 7-7   Flow-lift characteristics at constant pressure drop for uncharacterized valves.

across the valve.   At best the relation between flow and pressure drop for a given lift is similar to the orifice equation, which is inherently non-linear.   Because of the difficulty of analytic formulation, manufacturers have preferred to define the flow characteristics of their valves via graphs of the flows that result from various valve positions at constant pressure drop across the valve.   Typical characteristics for three valves are shown in Fig. 7-7 and for one characterized valve in Fig. 7-8.

The characteristic of the parabolic plug valve is referred to as an equal-percentage characteristic.   Ordinarily, this is the kind of behavior that is sought in all characterized valves.   The name *equal percentage* arises from the fact that the flow increments resulting from a given incremental change in lift are the same percentage of the actual flow regardless of whether the valve is nearly open or nearly closed.   Thus the valve has essentially constant sensitivity at all levels of flow.   This behavior is not true for the bevel plug valve or the weir valve, for example, where the valve sensitivity is excessively high at low flows but very poor at high flows.

Example 7-1   The first three lines of Table 7-1 give a comparison of the flow-lift behavior of a typical uncharacterized valve such as the bevel plug valve and a characterized valve with nearly equal percentage

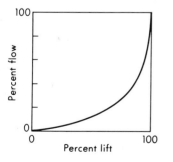

Figure 7-8   Flow-lift characteristic for parabolic plug valve.

Table 7-1   Control-valve sensitivity for various loads

Lift, percent of full range	10	15	20	80	85	90
Flow through bevel plug valve, percent of maximum flow	12	18	24	92	95	98
Flow through characterized valve, percent of maximum flow	3	4	5	46	51	69
Plug-valve sensitivity:						
Based on maximum flow		1.2			0.6	
Based on actual flow		6.7			0.63	
Characterized-valve sensitivity:						
Based on maximum flow		0.2			2.3	
Based on actual flow		5.0			4.5	

flow-lift behavior.   Estimate the sensitivities expressed as percent of load at lifts of 15 and 85 percent for these two valves.

Solution   The loads for these valves are given by the actual flows through valves in percent of the maximum possible flows.   At 15 percent lift the sensitivity of the bevel plug valve based on maximum flow is approximately $(24 - 12)/(20 - 10)$, or 1.2 percent, of the maximum flow for each percent change in lift.   Expressed as a percentage of the load, or actual flow rate, the sensitivity is $1.2(100)/18$, or 6.7 percent.   These values are listed in the table along with the corresponding values at 85 percent lift and those for the characterized valve at the same lifts.

It will be observed that the sensitivity of the bevel plug valve decreases by more than a factor of 10 when the load is increased from 15 to 85 percent of full flow, whereas the sensitivity of the characterized valve decreases by only 10 percent.

Since both the valve position, or lift, and the pressure drop across the valve may be changing in normal operation, the actual flow-lift behavior of a valve is more complicated than that given by either the orifice equation or the plots of flow-lift characteristics.   At particular operating levels the valve behavior may be approximated linearly by using the slopes of the flow-lift curve for the actual pressure drop across the valve and at the actual mean condition of lift.   This slope is the steady-state gain and the effective transfer function for the valve.   The valve dynamics ordinarily are too rapid to make any contributions to the control-loop dynamics.

7-9   *Control-valve selection*

The important factors to be considered in selecting proper control valves are (1) the rangeability of the process and the maximum specific range of flows required by the process, (2) the normal range of operating loads to be controlled, (3) the available pressure drops at the valve location at maximum flow and at minimum flow, and (4) the nature and condition of the fluid.

Obviously, the control-valve rangeability must exceed by some reasonable safety margin the rangeability of the process. A common practice is to equate valve turndown to process rangeability. For a valve turndown which is 70 percent of the valve rangeability, this practice results in a safety margin of over 40 percent in rangeability.

In addition to having sufficient rangeability, the valve must be able to moderate flows which are well below the minimum requirement of the process, and the maximum the valve will pass must exceed the peak requirement of the process.

For most process plants the normal range of operating loads is very narrow, and the control valves maintain nearly constant flow rates for long periods of time, changing appreciably only for starting up and shutting down the plant. Uncharacterized valves, sized to operate at 60 to 70 percent of full capacity, serve well for these plants.

There are many process plants, however, which operate for long periods of time at different load levels. The control valves for these plants may have to operate at 10 percent of capacity at times and at 60 percent of capacity at other times. Plants running batchwise frequently will have associated control circuits in which the control valve will have to accommodate a continuously changing load. A simple example would be a batch polymerizer which requires a large flow of coolant at the start of the polymerization and very little coolant at the termination. For plants like these, which are subject to large changes in operating loads, characterized valves having essentially equal percentage flow-lift characteristics are usually advantageous, since they provide a more constant fractional sensitivity at all operating levels.

The nature and condition of the fluid and the available pressure drop at the valve also will determine to some extent the style of valve that is chosen. For clear fluids at high pressure drop the double-seated plug valve or the rotary plug valve might be preferred, the latter if a high rangeability is desired. For slurries and particularly corrosive materials, pinch valves might be used.

The required flows and the available pressure drop determine the valve size. Ordinarily, the safest and simplest procedure in sizing valves is to use the tables, charts, or nomographs furnished by valve manufacturers.

The available pressure drop across the valve generally will not be constant for all flows, but will be a maximum for zero flow and lower for higher flows. If the pressure drop at maximum flow is less than half the pressure drop at zero flow, the flow-lift characteristic of the valve will be impaired. This fact may be appreciated from the following qualitative analysis. If the characteristics of the fluid-supply pump result in low delivery head at high flows, or if the supply line has appreciable resistance to flow, the available pressure drop at the valve will be low at high flows. A large valve, therefore, will be required to pass the desired maximum flows at the low pressure drop. At low flow rates through the large valve, the pressure drop will be high and small changes in valve lift will produce very large changes in flow rate. At high flow rates, larger changes in lift will be required to offset the decreasing pressure drop. The net effect is to limit the useful moderating or throttling range of the valve, and in an extreme case, where the ratio of maximum to minimum pressure drop is, say, 50, the valve approximates an on-off device.

Problems

7-1 A characterized valve has the following flow-lift properties at a pressure drop of 60 psi:

Percent flow	2.2	4.3	8.7	16.0	33.4	100
Percent lift	0	20	40	60	80	100

At a pressure drop of 100 psi the flow through the valve when wide open is 100 gpm. Estimate the valve gain for small perturbations in lift at 40 percent lift and 40 psi pressure drop and at 20 percent lift at 40 psi and also at 80 psi.

7-2 Sketch the flow-lift characteristics of the valve in Prob. 7-1 for the case where the pressure ahead of the valve is maintained at 60 psig and the valve discharges to the atmosphere through a nozzle which sustains a pressure drop of 16.7 psi at a flow of 7.0 gpm. The flow through the nozzle may be taken to be proportional to the square root of the pressure drop across the nozzle.

7-3 Repeat Prob. 7-2 for the case where a flow resistor with the same characteristics as the nozzle is inserted upstream of the valve. The discharge from the valve flows through the nozzle, but now the constant upstream pressure of 60 psig obtains just before the resistor.

7-4 Repeat Prob. 7-2 for the case where the upstream resistor lies in a bypass around the valve and the combined effluent from the valve and the bypass flows directly to the atmosphere. Plot this combined flow versus the valve lift. Note that this piping arrangement permits the moderation of larger flows than could be handled by the valve alone. What would you expect the combined flow-lift characteristics to be if all the effluent passed through the nozzle?

7-5   The gain of a flow control valve at a particular operating point is 2.7 gpm/ percent lift, and the valve actuator with a time constant of 0.1 min strokes the valve fully for pneumatic signals covering the standard range of 3 to 15 psi.   If the actuator is driven by a pneumatic controller with a proportional gain of 2.6 and a reset rate of 30 repeats per minute, and if the flow is metered by a differential-pressure cell mounted on an orifice upstream of the valve, what is the overall open-loop transfer function for the ratio of controller output at actuator input?   The DP cell has a very rapid response and generates a pneumatic signal 3 to 15 psi for the full range of flows from 0 to 100 gpm corresponding to the controller scale.

dynamics of
closed-loop systems

It has been emphasized that closed-loop control is an essential feature of economically feasible process systems. The feedback permits precise and efficient regulation without the need for elaborate appraisal of all contributory variables. Unfortunately, this same feedback makes it possible for control systems involving inherently stable and passive processes to become unstable. The following sections describe the dynamic characteristics of feedback control systems and the conditions under which instabilities occur. Analytical and graphical methods for determining limiting conditions of stability are presented, together with methods for determining transient responses analytically and from frequency-response characteristics.

8-1   Closed-loop transfer functions

For convenience in manipulation and without any sacrifice in generality, let us assume that the instrumentation in the simple process control system to be considered in this chapter is well suited to the process, with the result that the dynamics of the sensors, actuators, and valves may be neglected.   Figure 8-1 shows the block diagram for this control system.

The symbols in the figure have the same significance as before, namely:

r = reference signal, or set point
c = controlled variable
m = controller output
u = disturbance signal
G_c = controller-function-generator transfer function
G = process transfer function

Since there are two input signals and one response signal, there are two transfer functions for the feedback system, one relating response to set point and the other to disturbance.   For the response to disturbances, we take the set point to be constant, and therefore, in terms of perturbed variables, $r = 0$, $M = -G_cC$, and

$$C = G(M + U) \tag{8-1}$$

where the capitalized variables are Laplace-transformed quantities.

The controller transfer function $G_c = -M/C$ may be used to eliminate M from Eq. (8-1), with the result that

$$\frac{C}{U} = \frac{G}{1 + G_cG} \tag{8-2}$$

The ratio C/U is the *regulator ratio*.

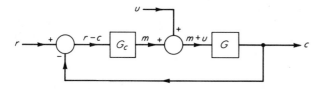

Figure 8-1   Typical process control system.

For the transfer function relating the system response to changes in set point, $u = 0$ and $C = GM$. Since

$$M = G_c(R - C) \tag{8-3}$$

we find

$$C = GM = G_cG(R - C)$$

and therefore

$$\frac{C}{R} = \frac{G_cG}{1 + G_cG} \tag{8-4}$$

This ratio C/R is the *control ratio.*

8-2   *Analytical approach to loop stability*

It was pointed out in Chap. 3 that all the information about the stability of the transient or dynamic response of a process system is contained in the characteristic equation obtained from the homogeneous differential equation of the system. This characteristic equation is identically the equation obtained by setting the polynomial in the denominator of the transfer function equal to zero.

The two transfer functions for the system of Fig. 8-1 have the same denominator, which is to be expected, because the stability characteristics of the system are not dependent on the nature or on the location of the forcing. Thus the characteristic equation of the system is

$$1 + G_cG = 0 \tag{8-5}$$

and the limiting condition of stability occurs when the roots of this equation are pure imaginary, since these roots are the coefficients on the exponents of the succession of exponential terms constituting the transient response.

If G is a known function of s, we can substitute $j\omega_0$ for s in Eq. (8-5) and determine the parameters of G_c which will make the system unstable. At the same time we can determine the ultimate frequency ω_0, which is the frequency of oscillation of the process variables at the limiting condition of stability.

As an example of the application of this analytical approach to the problem of gauging system stability, let us consider the simple case of a process consisting of three first-order transfer lags in series under control by a proportional controller.   For this case

$$G = \frac{1}{(1 + T_1 s)(1 + T_2 s)(1 + T_3 s)}$$ (8-6)

and

$$G_c = K_p$$ (8-7)

The characteristic equation becomes

$$1 + \frac{K_p}{\sum_3 (T) s^3 + \sum_2 (T) s^2 + \sum_1 (T) s + 1} = 0$$

or

$$\sum_3 (T) s^3 + \sum_2 (T) s^2 + \sum_1 (T) s + 1 + K_p = 0$$ (8-8)

where $\sum_n (T)$ means the summation of all possible combinations of T taken n at a time.   That is,

$$\sum_3 (T) = T_1 T_2 T_3$$

$$\sum_2 (T) = T_1 T_2 + T_2 T_3 + T_1 T_3$$

$$\sum_1 (T) = T_1 + T_2 + T_3$$

Substituting $j\omega_0$ for s and K_{p_0}, the ultimate proportional gain, for K_p, and collecting real and imaginary terms, we get

$$- \sum_2 (T)\omega_0^2 + 1 + K_{p_0} + j \left[- \sum_3 (T)\omega_0^3 + \sum_1 (T)\omega_0 \right] = 0$$

or since we cannot equate the real and imaginary parts, each of the parts must equal zero; hence

$$- \sum_2 (T)\omega_0^2 + 1 + K_{p_0} = 0$$ (8-9)

and

$$- \sum_3 (T)\omega_0{}^3 + \sum_1 (T)\omega_0 = 0 \tag{8-10}$$

From Eq. (8-10) we find that

$$\omega_0 = \sqrt{\dfrac{\sum\limits_1 (T)}{\sum\limits_3 (T)}} \tag{8-11}$$

and inserting this result in Eq. (8-9) gives

$$K_{p_0} = \dfrac{\sum\limits_1 (T) \sum\limits_2 (T)}{\sum\limits_3 (T)} - 1 \tag{8-12}$$

If the T are known, these two equations identify directly K_{p_0}, the smallest amount of proportioning action required to produce the limiting condition of stability, and ω_0, the frequency of cycling at that condition.

8-3   *Graphical approach to loop stability*

The results obtained by the analytical procedure in the preceding section may be obtained by graphical procedures, using either of the Nyquist diagrams or the Bode diagram.   For this purpose the inverse Nyquist diagram and the Bode diagram are particularly useful.   Figure 8-2 indicates the construction on the inverse Nyquist diagram, and Fig. 8-3 that on the Bode diagram, both for a typical third-order process controlled by proportional action only.

On Fig. 8-2 the ultimate proportional gain is found at the intersection of the process vector locus with the negative real axis.   The

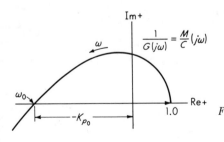

Figure 8-2   Limiting condition of stability on inverse Nyquist diagram.

frequency at the point of intersection is ω_0, the ultimate, or critical, frequency. This construction in effect satisfies Eq. (8-5), the characteristic equation of the system, written for $s = j\omega_0$, namely,

$$\frac{M}{C}(j\omega_0) = \frac{1}{G(j\omega_0)} = -G_c(j\omega_0) = -K_{p_0} \tag{8-13}$$

This equation as written implies that there are no externally imposed disturbances, but for stability analysis such disturbances are not relevant.

On Fig. 8-3 the construction also makes use of Eq. (8-5), but this time written as

$$G_c(j\omega_0)G(j\omega_0) = -1$$

which for this case is

$$K_{p_0}G(j\omega_0) = -1 \tag{8-14}$$

According to this equation, the limiting condition of stability occurs when the magnitude ratio is

$$|K_{p_0}G(j\omega_0)| = |-1| = 1 \tag{8-15}$$

and the phase angle at the same frequency is

$$\underline{/G(j\omega_0)} = -180° \tag{8-16}$$

which is the angle corresponding to a change in sign. The procedure for finding K_{p_0} is to locate the ultimate frequency ω_0 at the condition of phase

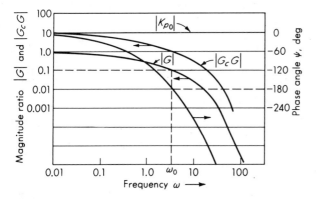

Figure 8-3 Limiting condition of stability on Bode diagram.

crossover given by Eq. (8-16) and at this frequency determine the gain margin of $G(j\omega_0)$ alone. This gain margin is precisely the signal amplification required in G_c, namely, K_{p_0}, to satisfy Eq. (8-15). In the figure the critical, or ultimate, frequency ω_0 is approximately 3 rad/min, and the open-loop magnitude ratio for the process alone, $|G|$, at this frequency is 0.1. The ultimate gain, then, according to Eq. (8-15), is

$$K_{p_0} = \frac{1}{|G(j\omega_0)|} = \frac{1}{0.1} = 10.$$

8-4   *Offset*

It was pointed out in Sec. 6-5 that the principal disadvantage of proportional control is that it tolerates offset, or steady-state, error. This characteristic may be defined quantitatively for the system of Fig. 8-1 by considering the equation for regulator performance:

$$\frac{C}{U} = \frac{G}{1 + G_c G} \tag{8-2}$$

If the process variable terms are perturbations about normal operating points, c may be regarded as the error, or deviation, resulting from load changes u. For a sustained load change of magnitude A, $U = A/s$, and the final steady value of c becomes the offset, or steady-state, error resulting from the load change. The final-value theorem of the Laplace transformation as given by Eq. (3-58) is

$$\lim_{s \to 0} sF(s) = \lim_{t \to \infty} f(t) \tag{3-58}$$

This equation may be applied directly to the case at hand to give

$$c_s = \lim_{t \to \infty} c = \lim_{s \to 0} sC$$

where c_s is the steady-state error. Since Eq. (8-2) for step forcing in u of A is

$$C = \frac{AG}{s(1 + G_c G)}$$

we have

$$c_s = \lim_{s \to 0} \frac{AG}{1 + G_c G}$$

Now the transfer function G, if it is written for normalized process variables as in Eq. (8-6), becomes unity in the limit as s approaches zero, which is the same condition as when ω approaches zero in the frequency plane. Therefore the offset is given by

$$c_s = \lim_{s \to 0} \frac{A}{1 + G_c} \tag{8-17}$$

and for the special case of proportional control,

$$c_s = \frac{A}{1 + K_p} \tag{8-18}$$

A large value of K_p will result in a small steady-state error, but if stability requirements make large values of K_p inaccessible, some error-integrating action will be required in the controller.

8-5 *Limiting condition of stability with integral control*

The control function for integral control is

$$G_c(s) = \frac{1}{T_I s} \tag{8-19}$$

where T_I is the integral time. Combining this equation with Eqs. (8-6) and (8-5) gives, for the third-order system with integral control,

$$1 + \frac{1}{T_I s} \frac{1}{\sum_3 (T)s^3 + \sum_2 (T)s^2 + \sum_1 (T)s + 1} = 0$$

and multiplying the resulting characteristic equation through by s and rearranging leads to

$$\sum_3 (T)s^4 + \sum_2 (T)s^3 + \sum_1 (T)s^2 + s + \frac{1}{T_I} = 0 \tag{8-20}$$

Substituting $s = j\omega_0$ and $T_I = T_{I_0}$ gives

$$\sum_3 (T)\omega_0^4 - j \sum_2 (T)\omega_0^3 - \sum_1 (T)\omega_0^2 + j\omega_0 + \frac{1}{T_{I_0}} = 0$$

and setting the real and imaginary parts equal to zero, we find

$$\sum_3 (T)\omega_0{}^4 - \sum_1 (T)\omega_0{}^2 + \frac{1}{T_{I_0}} = 0$$

and

$$-\sum_2 (T)\omega_0{}^3 + \omega_0 = 0$$

From the latter,

$$\omega_0 = \left[\sum_2 (T)\right]^{-\frac{1}{2}} \tag{8-21}$$

and inserting this into the real part,

$$\frac{\sum_3 (T)}{\left[\sum_2 (T)\right]^2} - \frac{\sum_1 (T)}{\sum_2 (T)} + \frac{1}{T_{I_0}} = 0$$

or

$$\frac{1}{T_{I_0}} = \frac{\sum_1 (T)}{\sum_2 (T)} - \frac{\sum_3 (T)}{\left[\sum_2 (T)\right]^2} \tag{8-22}$$

where T_{I_0} is the ultimate integral time.

Example 8-1   A liquid-flow control system consists of a differential-pressure-cell orifice meter, which generates pneumatic signals of 3 to 15 psig for flows of 0 to 120 gpm, and a valve and actuator, which produce flows of 1 to 85 gpm for pneumatic pressures of 3 to 15 psig on the actuator. The meter has a time constant of 0.6 sec, and the valve and actuator together have a time constant of 1 sec. Other elements in the system exert negligible effect on the dynamics of the system. If a pure integral controller is used to close the loop for this system, what integral time will make the system oscillate, and what will be the period of oscillation?

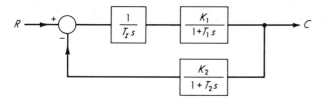

Figure 8-4   Block diagram for flow control system of Example
8-1.

Solution   Figure 8-4 shows a block diagram of the closed-loop
system with the actuator and valve transfer function designated by subscript 1 and that for the flowmeter by subscript 2.
The characteristic equation for this system is

$$1 + G_cG_1G_2 = 0$$

since the closed-loop transfer function is

$$\frac{C}{R} = \frac{G_cG_1}{1 + G_cG_1G_2}$$

where G_c = controller transfer function, $1/T_Is$
$\qquad G_1 = K_1/(1 + T_1s)$
$\qquad G_2 = K_2/(1 + T_2s)$
In terms of time constants and steady gains, the characteristic
equation is

$$1 + \frac{1}{T_Is} \frac{K_1K_2}{(1 + T_1s)(1 + T_2s)} = 0$$

or

$$T_I \sum_2 (T)s^3 + T_I \sum_1 (T)s^2 + T_Is + K_1K_2 = 0$$

In order to identify the condition of zero-damped oscillation, let
$s = j\omega_0$ and $T_I = T_{I_0}$.   Then

$$-jT_{I_0} \sum_2 (T)\omega_0{}^3 - T_{I_0} \sum_1 (T)\omega_0{}^2 + jT_{I_0}\omega_0 + K_1K_2 = 0$$

Whence, from the imaginary terms,

$$\omega_0 = \sqrt{\frac{1}{T_1T_2}}$$

and from the real terms,

$$T_{I_0} = \frac{K_1 K_2}{(T_1 + T_2)\omega^2} = \frac{K_1 K_2 T_1 T_2}{T_1 + T_2}$$

Now

$$K_1 = \frac{85 - 1}{15 - 3} = 7 \text{ gpm/psi}$$

$$K_2 = \frac{15 - 3}{120 - 0} = 0.1 \text{ psi/gpm}$$

$$T_1 = 1.0 \text{ sec} \qquad T_2 = 0.6 \text{ sec}$$

and hence

$$\omega_0 = \frac{1}{\sqrt{0.6}} = 1.29 \text{ rad/sec}$$

and the period of oscillation is $2\pi/1.29$, or 4.88 sec.
The ultimate integral time is

$$T_{I_0} = \frac{(7)(0.1)(1)(0.6)}{(1.6)} = 0.263 \text{ sec}$$

which corresponds to a setting in repeat rate of $60/0.263$, or 228 repeats per minute.

8-6   *Graphical construction for integral control*

The limiting values for ω_0 and T_{I_0} also may be obtained from the Nyquist diagram for integral control and the inverse Nyquist diagram for the process.   In Chap. 6 the Nyquist diagram for integral control, including the summer, was plotted in Fig. 6-10 as $(M/C)(j\omega)$, the ratio of controller output to controlled variable input at constant reference signal.   But this ratio is also the function which is plotted for the process on the inverse Nyquist diagram.   The intersection of these two vector loci identifies the limiting condition of stability for the feedback control system composed of the two elements described by the two loci, just as in Sec. 8-3.   Figure 8-5 shows the construction.
The construction for determining T_{I_0} and ω_0 on the Bode diagram

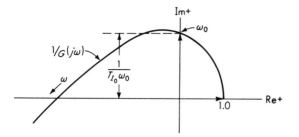

Figure 8-5 Limiting condition of stability for integral control.

is shown in Fig. 8-6. Since the angle of $G_c(j\omega)$ is $-90°$ for all frequencies, the critical phase angle for the process $G(j\omega)$ is $-90°$. At the critical frequency, where the process angle is $-90°$, the process gain margin is marked GM. For instability, the controller gain, in this case $1/T_{I_0}\omega_0$, must match the attenuation corresponding to the gain margin. Thus, if the open-loop process gain at phase crossover is 0.4, the gain margin is $1/0.4$, or 2.5, and hence $1/T_{I_0}\omega_0 = 2.5$.

8-7 *Proportional plus integral control*

When only one control mode is used with a given process, there is a single condition in the controller which will make the controlled system just unstable. If more than a single control mode is used, there are an infinite number of settings which will produce the limiting condition of stability. This situation is seen clearly in Fig. 8-7, which is the inverse

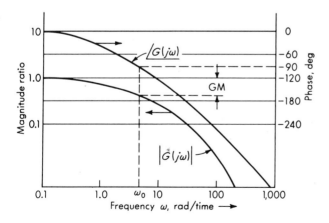

Figure 8-6 Ultimate stability with integral control.

Nyquist diagram for a third-order process.   Every point on the process vector locus lying in the second quadrant can be matched by a resultant vector for combinations of proportional plus integral control.   One such vector is shown at ω_0, having an imaginary part $1/T_{I_0}\omega_0$ due to the integral action and the real part $-K_{p_0}$ due to the proportional action.

Since the speed of response is related to the critical frequency ω_0, it can be seen from the figure that the effect of adding integral action to proportional action is to decrease the critical frequency, and hence decrease the speed of response from that which would obtain with proportional control alone.   Furthermore, the overall controller gain given by the length of the control vector typically will be less than the ultimate proportional gain for pure proportional control.   Thus, for processes with frequency-response characteristics similar to those of the locus in Fig. 8-7, which characteristics are typical of virtually all common process systems, integral control has a destabilizing effect.

8-8   Three-mode control

The principal function of integral control is to eliminate offset.   In order to increase the speed of response, it is necessary to add derivative action.   The combination of proportional control, integral control, and derivative control is called three-mode, or PID, control.   As in the case of proportional plus integral control, there are an infinite number of combinations of the control-mode parameters K_p, T_I, and T_D which will make a given closed-loop control system unstable.   One such combination is illustrated in Fig. 8-8.

The effect of the derivative action is to increase the critical frequency ω_0 and also increase K_{p_0}, the ultimate proportional gain.   These effects result from the fact that the addition of derivative action rotates the control vector into the third quadrant of the inverse Nyquist diagram

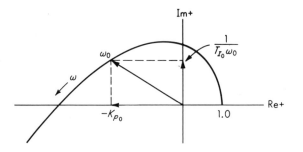

Figure 8-7   Proportional plus integral control.

for the process as shown on Fig. 8-8.   In this example the addition of the derivative action in the amount $K_{p_0}T_{D_0}\omega_0$ permits the proportional gain to be increased more than one-third over the ultimate proportional gain for proportional control alone.

The shape of the vector locus for the process, that is to say, the characteristics of the process, determines how much advantage results from the addition of the derivative action.   If the inverse Nyquist diagram for the process does not increase its distance from the origin significantly in passing through the third quadrant, as is the case for systems dominated by time delays, or if the frequency increases slowly in that quadrant, there may be no advantage in adding the derivative action.

8-9   Routh-Hurwitz criterion

The limiting conditions of stability for the three-mode control system in the preceding section may be determined analytically by substituting $j\omega_0$ for s in the characteristic equation and separately examining the real and imaginary parts as in Sec. 8-5.   Similarly, the Bode diagram may be used, although for combined modes of control it is somewhat less convenient for purposes of illustration than the polar diagram.

There is yet another way of solving the stability problem.   It will be recalled that the property of the characteristic equation of a feedback control system which makes for instability is the occurrence of roots which are positive and real or which have positive real parts.   Therefore any rule or theorem of algebra which can identify the existence of real positive roots in a polynomial can be used to determine the control parameters necessary for the limiting condition of stability.   Such a rule is the basis for the Routh-Hurwitz criterion of stability.

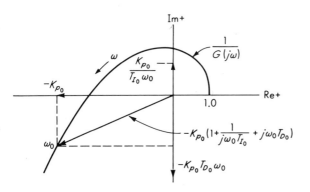

Figure 8-8   Nyquist diagram for ideal three-mode control.

The characteristic equation for a single feedback loop is given by Eq. (8-5) as

$$1 + G_cG = 0 \qquad\qquad (8\text{-}5)$$

In general, this equation is a polynomial in s, or if it contains transcendental terms such as e^{-Ts}, these terms can be expanded, and the resulting equation will be a polynomial in s of the form

$$a_ns^n + a_{n-1}s^{n-1} + \cdots + a_0 = 0 \qquad\qquad (8\text{-}23)$$

For convenience in manipulation and clarity in exposition we consider the fourth-degree polynomial,

$$a_4s^4 + a_3s^3 + a_2s^2 + a_1s + a_0 = 0 \qquad\qquad (8\text{-}24)$$

The first step is to construct an array based on the Hurwitzian determinant. In the top row we list the coefficients on alternate terms in the polynomial, beginning with the highest-degree term. In the second row we list the remaining terms, and then we evaluate terms for the rest of the rows in the array according to the formulation shown in Table 8-1. The coefficients connected by the dashed lines are multiplied together and subtracted from the product of the coefficients connected by the solid lines, and the resulting difference is divided by the coefficient in the preceding row and same column as the desired term. Thus, to obtain

Table 8-1   *Routh-Hurwitz array for fourth-degree polynomial*

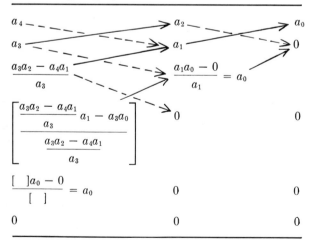

the first term of the third row in the table, the coefficients in the two preceding rows connected by a solid line, namely, a_3 and a_2, are multiplied together; the coefficients connected by a dashed line, namely, a_4 and a_1, are also multiplied together, and then subtracted from a_3a_2; and finally, this difference, namely, $a_3a_2 - a_4a_1$, is divided by the coefficient in the preceding row (row 2) and in the same column (column 1) namely, a_3.

The construction of the array is terminated when all terms in the last row are zeros. It can be seen from the form of the matrix that there must be $n + 1$ rows and $n + 1$ columns, when n is the degree of the polynomial. Each row may be regarded as a polynomial decreasing in degree by one in each step down the matrix.

If two successive rows in the matrix are term-by-term proportional, the next row will be all zeros, and the polynomial corresponding to the second of the proportional rows will be a factor of the original polynomial. In order to complete the matrix, the row of zeros must be replaced by the derivative of the polynomial which is the factor of the original equation.

If a zero occurs in the first term of a row, a small positive number is substituted for the zero, and the construction of the array can be continued.

Routh's criterion states that the number of changes in algebraic sign in going down the first column of the array is equal to the number of roots having positive real parts. A corollary is that there are no positive real roots or roots with real positive parts if there are no missing terms in the polynomial and if all the terms in the left-hand column of the array are positive.

For the characteristic equation given by the fourth-degree polynomial arrayed in Table 8-1, the limiting conditions for stability must correspond to

$$a_3a_2 - a_4a_1 = 0 \tag{8-25}$$

and

$$\frac{a_3a_2 - a_4a_1}{a_3} a_1 - a_3a_0 = 0$$

which may be rearranged to

$$a_1a_2a_3 - a_1{}^2a_4 - a_0a_3{}^2 = 0 \tag{8-26}$$

Since both a_3 and a_0 must be positive because each occurs alone in the first column, the satisfaction of Eq. (8-25) would require a condition of definite instability according to Eq. (8-26) as originally written, and hence Eq. (8-26) is a more discriminating gauge of the limiting stability.

In certain control systems there may be two limiting conditions of stability, corresponding, for example, to upper and lower limits on the controller gain. The control of an exothermic chemical reaction may require a certain minimum sensitivity or gain in the controller below which the reaction would run away or die out when perturbed. On the other hand, if the controller gain is set above the ultimate gain, the system again will be unstable. Routh's criterion can identify both limiting conditions. An interesting example occurs in Prob. 8-7.

Let us consider the control of the third-order system defined by Eq. (8-6), using ideal three-mode control. The characteristic equation for the closed-loop system is

$$1 + K_p \left(1 + \frac{1}{T_I s} + T_D s\right) \frac{1}{\sum_3 (T)s^3 + \sum_2 (T)s^2 + \sum_1 (T)s + 1} = 0$$

which may be rearranged into the form of Eq. (8-23), namely,

$$\sum_3 (T)s^4 + \sum_2 (T)s^3 + \left[\sum_1 (T) + K_p T_D\right] s^2 + (1 + K_p)s$$

$$+ \frac{K_p}{T_I} = 0 \quad (8\text{-}27)$$

Substituting the appropriate coefficients in Eq. (8-26) gives

$$(1 + K_{p_0}) \left[\sum_1 (T) + K_{p_0} T_{D_0}\right] \left[\sum_2 (T)\right] - (1 + K_{p_0})^2 \sum_3 (T)$$

$$- \frac{K_{p_0}}{T_{I_0}} \left[\sum_2 (T)\right]^2 = 0 \quad (8\text{-}28)$$

This equation is cumbersome, but it shows that increasing T_D makes the equation more positive, and hence derivative action is a stabilizing effect, whereas increasing $1/T_I$ is destabilizing. For given specifications of two of the control parameters, the third can be computed readily. In order to calculate the critical frequency for a particular combination of control modes, however, an additional relationship is required. This relationship could be the inverse Nyquist diagram or the Bode diagram for the process, or it could be obtained from the substitution of $j\omega_0$ for s in the characteristic equation.

Using this last strategy, we find, from Eq. (8-27),

$$\sum_3 (T)\omega_0{}^4 - j\sum_2 (T)\omega_0 - \left[\sum_1 (T) + K_{p_0}T_{D_0}\right]\omega_0{}^2$$

$$+ j(1 + K_{p_0})\omega_0 + \frac{K_{p_0}}{T_{I_0}} = 0$$

the real part of which gives

$$\sum_3 (T)\omega_0{}^4 - \left[\sum_1 (T) + K_{p_0}T_{D_0}\right]\omega_0{}^2 + \frac{K_{p_0}}{T_{I_0}} = 0 \qquad (8\text{-}29)$$

and the imaginary part gives

$$-\sum_2 (T)\omega_0{}^3 + (1 + K_{p_0})\omega_0 = 0$$

or

$$\omega_0 = \sqrt{\frac{1 + K_{p_0}}{\sum_2 (T)}} \qquad (8\text{-}30)$$

This equation shows that the critical frequency, and consequently the speed of response of the control system, increases with increasing K_{p_0} for third-order processes characterized by the transfer-function equation (8-6). By solving Eq. (8-29) for K_{p_0}, it can be shown that K_{p_0} can be increased by increasing either T_{I_0} or T_{D_0}, that is, by decreasing the integrating action or by increasing the derivative action.

The method of Routh is useful, principally, for solving the stability problem, either determining whether a given system is stable or determining what conditions will make a given system unstable. For complex systems it may be less convenient than graphical methods using polar diagrams or Bode plots, and by itself it does not lead directly to useful designs.

Example 8-2 The characteristic equation of a proposed feedback system is

$$s^5 + 2s^4 + 2s^3 + 4s^2 + 5s + 10 = 0$$

Is this system stable?

Solution   The first row of the array is formed from the coefficients on alternate terms, beginning with the first term s^5, and the second row, beginning with the second term $2s^4$.

$$
\begin{array}{ccc}
1 & 2 & 5 \\
2 & 4 & 10 \\
\dfrac{(2)(2) - (1)(4)}{2} = 0 & \dfrac{(4)(5) - (2)(10)}{4} = 0 & 0
\end{array}
$$

Now we must replace these zeros by the coefficients of the derivative of the polynomial $2s^4 + 4s^2 + 10$, namely,

$$(2)(4) = 8 \qquad (4)(2) = 8 \qquad 0$$

The rest of the array may now be computed.

$$
\begin{array}{ccc}
\dfrac{(8)(4) - (2)(8)}{8} = 2 & \dfrac{(8)(10) - 0}{8} = 10 & 0 \\[2ex]
\dfrac{(2)(8) - (8)(10)}{2} = -32 & 0 & 0 \\[2ex]
0 & 0 & 0
\end{array}
$$

There is one change of algebraic sign in the first column in going from 2 to -32, and hence there is one positive root, and the system is unstable.

8-10   *Transient response of closed-loop systems*

The limiting condition of stability is a useful index of controllability for feedback control systems, but it is not a desirable condition for operating process systems.   As is discussed in detail in Chap. 9, the typically desired behavior in process control systems is that the controlled variable register closely with the set point and recover quickly from disturbances imposed on the system.   The manner in which the system recovers from disturbances is governed by the characteristic equation of the system, and particularly by the roots of that equation.

In principle, the transient response of a closed-loop process system can be determined from the transfer function of the system through use of the inverse Laplace transformation.   In practice, it is not often very convenient to arrange the transformed terms in forms which can be inverted by inspection.   This difficulty can be seen from a consideration of the third-order process defined by Eq. (8-6) under proportional control alone.   The response of this system to unit impulse forcing in the disturbance input u is given by the solution of Eq. (8-2), with U set equal to 1.0, namely,

$$C = \frac{G}{1 + GG_c} U = \frac{G}{1 + GG_c} \tag{8-31}$$

which, for this system, is

$$C = \frac{1}{\sum_3 (T)s^3 + \sum_2 (T)s^2 + \sum_1 (T)s + 1 + K_p} \tag{8-32}$$

We can write this equation in factored form as

$$C = \frac{1}{(s + s_1)(s + s_2)(s + s_3)} \tag{8-33}$$

where $-s_1$, $-s_2$, and $-s_3$ are the roots of the polynomial in the denominator of Eq. (8-32).   The inverse transform of this function may be obtained directly from Table 8-1, but the roots must be extracted first.

Example 8-3   Compute the response to a unit impulse disturbance in set point which is imposed on a third-order process characterized by time constants of 1, 4, and 10 sec and controlled by a proportional controller with a gain of 8.0.

Solution   For this system Eqs. (8-32) and (8-33) are appropriate. If we expand the denominator of the latter equation and equate the coefficients on the various powers of s to the coefficients on the corresponding terms in Eq. (8-32), we find

$$s_1 + s_2 + s_3 = \frac{T_1T_2 + T_2T_3 + T_1T_3}{T_1T_2T_3} \tag{8-34}$$

$$s_1s_2 + s_2s_3 + s_1s_3 = \frac{T_1 + T_2 + T_3}{T_1T_2T_3} \tag{8-35}$$

$$s_1s_2s_3 = \frac{1 + K_p}{T_1T_2T_3} \tag{8-36}$$

A typical practical control-system design requires that the responses to disturbances be slightly underdamped.   Two of the three roots of the characteristic equation therefore must be conjugate complex to contribute a damped oscillatory mode to the response, and the third root must provide additional damping.   Thus we may set

$$s_1 = \alpha_1 \qquad s_2 = \alpha_2 + j\beta \qquad s_3 = \alpha_2 - j\beta$$

where α_1 and α_2 are damping factors, and β is the damped frequency of the response.   Making these substitutions for the s and inserting the numerical values for the T, taking $T_1 = 1$, $T_2 = 4$, and $T_3 = 10$, and for K_p in Eqs. (8-34) to (8-36), gives

$$\alpha_1 + 2\alpha_2 = 1.35 \tag{8-37}$$

$$2\alpha_1\alpha_2 + \alpha_2{}^2 + \beta^2 = 0.375 \tag{8-38}$$

and

$$\alpha_2{}^2 + \beta^2 = \frac{0.225}{\alpha_1} \tag{8-39}$$

Subtract Eq. (8-39) from Eq. (8-38), and between the result of this subtraction and Eq. (8-37) eliminate α_2, to get the cubic equation

$$\alpha_1{}^3 - 1.35\alpha_1{}^2 + 0.375\alpha_1 = 0.225 \tag{8-40}$$

Since α_1 is a real positive number, we need determine only the real positive root of Eq. (8-40).   A simple procedure is to use Newton's method of approximation.   First try $\alpha_1 = 1.0$, for which the left-hand side of the equation is 0.025, which is too low.   For $\alpha_1 = 2.0$ the result is 3.75, which is too high.   Now assume $\alpha_1 = 1.0 + y$; inset this value in Eq. (8-40); and solve for y after rejecting all terms in y higher than first degree.
      Thus $y = 0.200/0.675 = 0.30$, and $\alpha_1 = 1.0 + 0.30$, or 1.30.   Now assume $\alpha_1 = 1.30 + y$ and repeat the procedure to find $y = 0.092$ and $\alpha_1 = 1.30 - 0.092 = 1.208$.   Repeat the procedure once more, and refine the estimate to

$$\alpha_1 = 1.20$$

Insert this value in Eq. (8-37) to get

$$\alpha_2 = 0.075$$

and insert both values in Eq. (8-38) to get $\beta = 0.441$ rad/sec.   Thus

$$s_1 = 1.20$$
$$s_2 = 0.075 + j0.441$$
$$s_3 = 0.075 - j0.441$$

According to Table 3-1, the inverse transformation of Eq. (8-33) is

$$c(t) = - \frac{(s_3 - s_2)e^{-s_1 t} + (s_1 - s_3)e^{-s_2 t} + (s_2 - s_1)e^{-s_3 t}}{(s_3 - s_2)(s_1 - s_3)(s_2 - s_1)} \tag{8-41}$$

In terms of the damping factors and damped frequencies,

$$s_3 - s_2 = -j2\beta$$

$$s_1 - s_3 = \alpha_1 - \alpha_2 + j\beta$$

$$s_2 - s_1 = \alpha_2 - \alpha_1 + j\beta$$

and inserting these quantities in Eq. (8-41) with appropriate cancellations of common factors and with multiplications and collections of terms, there results

$$c(t) = \frac{e^{-\alpha_1 t}}{(\alpha_2 - \alpha_1)^2 + \beta^2} + \frac{1}{2\beta} \frac{-\beta - j(\alpha_2 - \alpha_1)}{\beta^2 + (\alpha_2 - \alpha_1)^2} e^{(-\alpha_2 - j\beta)t}$$

$$+ \frac{1}{2\beta} \frac{-\beta + j(\alpha_2 - \alpha_1)}{\beta^2 + (\alpha_2 - \alpha_1)^2} e^{(-\alpha_2 + j\beta)t}$$

Application of Euler's equation to the imaginary exponentials, followed by expansion of the resulting expression, leads to a purely real sine and cosine function

$$c(t) = \frac{e^{-\alpha_1 t}}{(\alpha_2 - \alpha_1)^2 + \beta^2} + \frac{e^{-\alpha_2 t}}{\beta[(\alpha_2 - \alpha_1)^2 + \beta^2]}$$

$$[-\beta \cos \beta t - (\alpha_2 - \alpha_1) \sin \beta t]$$

which, by the trigonometric identity for the sine of a sum of two angles, reduces to

$$c(t) = \frac{e^{-\alpha_1 t}}{(\alpha_2 - \alpha_1)^2 + \beta^2} - \frac{e^{-\alpha_2 t}}{\beta[(\alpha_2 - \alpha_1)^2 + \beta^2]} \sin (\beta t + \psi) \tag{8-42}$$

where

$$\psi = \tan^{-1} \frac{\beta}{\alpha_2 - \alpha_1}$$

The signs of the numerator and denominator of the arc tangent must be separately identified to indicate the proper quadrant of the angle ψ, in this case the second quadrant, since $\psi = \tan^{-1}(0.441/-1.125)$. Inserting numerical values for the two α and the β leads to

$$c(t) = 0.683e^{-1.20t} - 1.87e^{-0.075t} \sin (0.441t + 2.767)$$

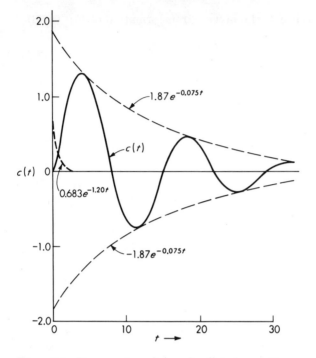

Figure 8-9   Response to unit impulse disturbance, Example 8-3.

This equation is sketched in Fig. 8-9.   The manner of sketching is indicated on the figure.   First, envelopes $\pm 1.87e^{-0.075t}$ and the decay term $0.683e^{-1.20t}$ are drawn, using the rules for first order responses. The time to the first peak is found by setting $0.441t + 2.767$ equal to $3\pi/2$, corresponding to minus unity for the sine function.   Since the separate decay term has negligible effect after the first few seconds, the times to successive zeros of the response are identified by setting the angle $0.441t + 2.767$ equal to multiples of π.   The response curve is then sketched in between the envelope curves, except for the small correction at the first peak, due to the separate decay term.   Note that the period of oscillation is $2\pi/\beta$ sec.

8-11   *Partial-fraction expansion*

For systems more complicated than the system of Example 8-3, the algebraic manipulations required to determine the transient response analytically can become quite tedious.   One useful technique is to expand complicated transforms into partial fractions which can be inverted easily.

Suppose we wish to obtain the inverse transform of the function

$$C(s) = \frac{p(s)}{q(s)} \tag{8-43}$$

where $p(s)$ and $q(s)$ are polynomials in s. If the ratio of these polynomials is an improper fraction, that is, $p(s)$ of greater degree than $q(s)$, it would be convenient to carry out the indicated division to get a new polynomial plus a proper fraction.

Assuming the fraction in Eq. (8-43) is proper, the roots of the denominator are obtained by conventional methods, and the polynomial is expressed in factored form as

$$q(s) = (s + s_1)(s + s_2) \cdots (s + s_n)$$

where the roots are $-s_1$, $-s_2$, etc. The fraction in Eq. (8-43) may now be written

$$\frac{p(s)}{q(s)} = \frac{A_1}{s + s_1} + \frac{A_2}{s + s_2} + \cdots + \frac{A_n}{s + s_n} \tag{8-44}$$

where the A are found from

$$A_j = \lim_{s \to -s_j} \frac{p(s)(s + s_j)}{q(s)} \tag{8-45}$$

Equation (8-45) may be derived from Eq. (8-44) by multiplying both sides of the latter through by $s + s_j$ and setting s equal to $-s_j$. All terms on the right-hand side become zero except for A_j, and the left side is identically the right side of Eq. (8-45). In evaluating Eq. (8-45), first cancel out the $s + s_j$ factor in $q(s)$ with the $s + s_j$ term in the numerator.

The foregoing expressions are valid for nonrepeating roots, that is, $s_1 \neq s_2 \neq s_3 \neq \cdots$. If there are repeating roots, the procedure must be altered slightly. For example, if the ith root is repeated n times, the A term for the first of the ith roots is given by

$$A_{i_1} = \left[\frac{p(s)(s + s_i)^n}{q(s)} \right]_{s=-s_i} \tag{8-46}$$

and the term for the jth repetition of the ith root is

$$A_{i_j} = \left[\frac{1}{(j-1)!} \frac{d^{j-1}}{ds^{j-1}} \frac{p(s)(s + s_i)^n}{q(s)} \right]_{s=-s_j} \tag{8-47}$$

where d^{j-1}/ds^{j-1} is the jth-minus-1 derivative with respect to s.

Example 8-4 Solve the problem in Example 8-3 using partial fractions.

Solution The transformed equation for the response to a unit impulse is the transfer function C/U, and hence, as before,

$$C = \frac{1}{(s + \alpha_1)(s + \alpha_2 + j\beta)(s + \alpha_2 - j\beta)}$$

and the partial-fraction expansion is

$$C = \frac{A_1}{s + \alpha_1} + \frac{A_2}{s + \alpha_2 + j\beta} + \frac{A_3}{s + \alpha_2 - j\beta}$$

According to Eq. (8-45),

$$A_1 = \lim_{s \to -\alpha_1} [C(s + \alpha_1)]$$

or

$$A_1 = \frac{1}{(\alpha_2 - \alpha_1 + j\beta)(\alpha_2 - \alpha_1 - j\beta)} = \frac{1}{(\alpha_2 - \alpha_1)^2 + \beta^2}$$

Similarly,

$$A_2 = \lim_{s \to -\alpha_2 - j\beta} \frac{1}{(s + \alpha_1)(s + \alpha_2 - j\beta)}$$

$$= \frac{1}{[-(\alpha_2 - \alpha_1) - j\beta](-2j\beta)} = \frac{1}{2\beta[j(\alpha_2 - \alpha_1) - \beta]}$$

and

$$A_3 = \frac{1}{[-(\alpha_2 - \alpha_1) + j\beta](2j\beta)} = \frac{1}{-2\beta[j(\alpha_2 - \alpha_1) + \beta]}$$

With the substitution of a for $\alpha_2 - \alpha_1$ and $\beta_0{}^2$ for $(\alpha_2 - \alpha_1)^2 + \beta^2$, the expanded equation for C is

$$C = \frac{1}{\beta_0{}^2(s + \alpha_1)} + \frac{1}{2\beta(ja - \beta)(s + \alpha_2 + j\beta)}$$

$$+ \frac{1}{-2\beta(ja + \beta)(s + \alpha_2 - j\beta)}$$

The inverse transformation, term by term, then, is

$$c(t) = \frac{e^{-\alpha_1 t}}{\beta_0{}^2} + \frac{e^{(-\alpha_2 - j\beta)t}}{2\beta(ja - \beta)} - \frac{e^{(-\alpha_2 + j\beta)t}}{2\beta(ja + \beta)}$$

Rewrite the last two terms as

$$\frac{(-ja - \beta)e^{(-\alpha_2 - j\beta)t}}{2\beta\beta_0{}^2} - \frac{(-ja + \beta)e^{(-\alpha_2 + j\beta)t}}{2\beta\beta_0{}^2}$$

and consolidate to

$$\frac{e^{-\alpha_2 t}}{2\beta\beta_0{}^2}[-(ja + \beta)(\cos \beta t - j \sin \beta t) + (ja - \beta)(\cos \beta t + j \sin \beta t)]$$

which reduces to

$$-\frac{e^{-\alpha_2 t}}{\beta\beta_0{}^2} \sin \left(\beta t + \tan^{-1} \frac{\beta}{a} \right)$$

and hence

$$c(t) = \frac{e^{-\alpha_1 t}}{(\alpha_2 - \alpha_1)^2 + \beta^2} - \frac{e^{-\alpha_2 t}}{\beta[(\alpha_2 - \alpha_1)^2 + \beta^2]} \sin \left(\beta t + \tan^{-1} \frac{\beta}{\alpha_2 - \alpha_1} \right)$$

which is the same expression as in Example 8-3.

8-12   *Transient response from frequency response*

It is seldom required that the transient characteristics of a con-trolled process system be known precisely.   More usually what is required is that the response of the system to disturbances stabilize reasonably quickly without excessive excursions of the controlled variables.   The rules for designing control systems using frequency-response characteriza-tion, which are discussed in detail in the next chapter, are aimed quite specifically at producing this kind of response.   Therefore, if we design a system using these rules, we can make some inferences about the nature of the transient response as listed below, although for particular cases the inferences may be unprecise.

1   In response to step forcings, the controlled-variable overshoot will equal, approximately, the maximum closed-loop magnitude ratio when that ratio is in the range 1.20 to 1.30.   Thus, if $|(C/R)(j\omega)|_{max} = 1.3$ for a particular process control system, a step change in the set point r will result in a transient response in the controlled variable c which will overshoot the final steady value of c by, roughly, 30 percent of the total change in c resulting from the change in reference signal.

2   The frequency of the transient response will lie between the fre-quencies at phase crossover and gain crossover for the open-loop system.

This inference says that the damped frequency of response of the controlled system will be somewhat less than the critical frequency of the system.

3 For typically underdamped responses of the controlled process variable, the subsidence ratio, namely, the ratio of the magnitudes of successive peaks in the decaying response, will be about 3:1.

8-13 *Closed-loop frequency-response characteristics*

In order to gauge the maximum overshoot that might occur in a process control system by means of the inference in the preceding section, it is necessary to know the frequency-response characteristics of the closed-loop system. If the open-loop frequency-response characteristics are known for all elements in the system, the corresponding closed-loop characteristics may be computed without difficulty. A particularly simple graphical technique may be used if the closed-loop characteristics are sought for the servo problem, namely, for the control ratio $|(C/R)(j\omega)|$.

Consider the case of unity feedback shown in Fig. 8-10. The closed-loop magnitude ratio for this system is

$$M = \left| \frac{C}{R}(j\omega) \right| = \left| \frac{G(j\omega)}{1 + G(j\omega)} \right| \tag{8-48}$$

But on the Nyquist diagram, or G plane, a point on the open-loop locus $G(j\omega)$ is given by $x + jy$; hence Eq. (8-48) may be written

$$M = \left| \frac{x + jy}{1 + x + jy} \right| \tag{8-49}$$

By separating the real and imaginary parts, squaring them, and setting the sum of the squares equal to M^2, we obtain, with some rearrangement, the equation of a circle at constant M.

$$y^2 + \left(x + \frac{M^2}{M^2 - 1} \right)^2 = \frac{M^2}{(M^2 - 1)^2} \tag{8-50}$$

Thus, on the Nyquist diagram, lines of constant closed-loop magnitude ratio are circles centered on the real axis at $-M^2/(M^2 - 1)$, with radii equal to $M/(M^2 - 1)$. The intersections of the open-loop vector locus, $G(j\omega)$, with these circles identifies the corresponding closed-loop magni-

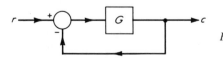

Figure 8-10 Simple closed loop with unity feedback.

tude ratios as shown in Fig. 8-11. Note that the maximum closed-loop magnitude ratio, usually designated M_p, occurs where the particular open-loop locus $G(j\omega)$ is just tangent to the $M = 1.3$ circle. The frequency at this condition is marked ω_r, the *resonant frequency* of the closed-loop system.

Loci of constant closed-loop phase angle are also circles on the G plane. The closed-loop angle in terms of the coordinates of the open-loop vector is

$$\Big/\frac{G}{1+G} = \psi = \Big/\frac{x+jy}{1+x+jy} \tag{8-51}$$

Let $\tan \psi = a$. Then, since

$$\frac{x+jy}{1+x+jy}\frac{1+x-jy}{1+x-jy} = \frac{x(1+x)+y^2+jy}{(1+x)^2+y^2}$$

we have

$$a = \frac{\text{Im}}{\text{Re}} = \frac{y}{x(1+x)+y^2} \tag{8-52}$$

or

$$y^2 - \frac{y}{a} + x^2 + x = 0$$

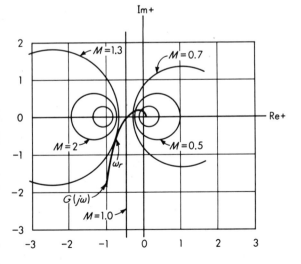

Figure 8-11   Constant-M lines on G plane.

This equation may be converted to a sum of two squared terms by adding $(1/2a)^2 + (1/2)^2$ to both sides, giving

$$\left(y - \frac{1}{2a}\right)^2 + \left(x + \frac{1}{2}\right)^2 = \frac{1}{4a^2} + \frac{1}{4} = \frac{1}{4}\frac{a^2 + 1}{a^2} \tag{8-53}$$

Thus lines of constant closed-loop phase angle on the G plane are circles of radius $(1/2a)\sqrt{a^2 + 1}$ and with centers at $j/2a$ on the vertical line at $-\frac{1}{2}$.

All the circles pass through 0 and -1 on the real axis. For angles of zero, $\pm 180°$, and multiples thereof, the circles are coincident with the real axis, and for $\pm 90°$, the circle is centered on the real axis and the radius is $\frac{1}{2}$. Typical circles are shown in Fig. 8-12.

8-14   Constant-M circles for inverse Nyquist diagram

The forcing in set point required to produce unit response in the simple closed-loop system of Fig. 8-10 is

$$\frac{R}{C} = \frac{1 + G}{G} = \frac{1}{G} + 1 \tag{8-54}$$

On the inverse Nyquist diagram, or G^{-1} plane, the coordinates of the open-loop transfer function $1/G$ are given by $x + jy$, and hence the

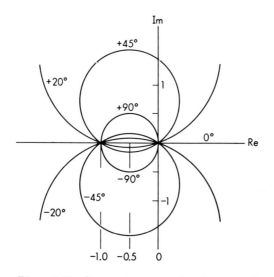

Figure 8-12   Constant-phase-angle circles on G plane.

magnitude ratio for the closed loop is

$$\left| \frac{R}{C} \right| = \frac{1}{M} = |x + jy + 1|$$

and

$$\frac{1}{M^2} = (x + 1)^2 + y^2 \tag{8-55}$$

Thus, on the G^{-1} plane, the constant-M loci are concentric circles centered on the real axis at -1.0, with radii equal to $1/M$. Figure 8-13 shows a few circles and a typical open-loop vector locus. Again, the intersection of this locus with a particular circle identifies the closed-loop magnitude ratio for the particular open-loop inverse Nyquist transfer function $1/G$.

Lines of constant phase angle for the closed loop on the G^{-1} plane may be found in the same manner as was used for the G plane.

$$\underline{/\frac{1}{G} + 1} = \underline{/x + jy + 1} = \tan^{-1} \frac{y}{x + 1}$$

whence, for $\tan \psi = a$,

$$y = ax + a \tag{8-56}$$

Thus lines of constant phase angle for the closed loop are straight lines on the G^{-1} plane radiating from the point -1.0 on the real axis as shown in Fig. 8-14. Since the slope of these lines is $a = \tan \psi$, the phase angle for each line is the angle the line makes with the real axis.

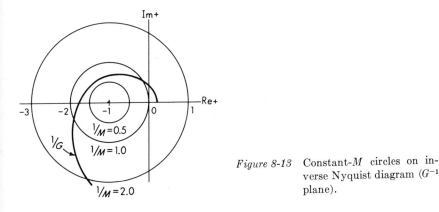

Figure 8-13 Constant-M circles on inverse Nyquist diagram (G^{-1} plane).

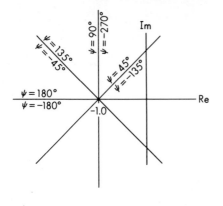

Figure 8-14 Lines of constant closed-loop phase angle on G^{-1} plane.

8-15   Nichols chart

Lines of constant closed-loop magnitude ratio, together with lines of constant closed-loop phase angle, may be drawn on a chart with the logarithm of the open-loop magnitude ratio as ordinate and the open-loop phase angle as abscissa. This construction, which results in what is called a Nichols, or Black-Nichols, chart, is shown in Fig. 8-15 for open-loop phase angle from 0 to $-180°$. In work with servomechanisms, the ordinate scale is commonly expressed in decibels.

Since the Nichols chart repeats itself every 360°, the section of the chart from -180 to $-360°$ is a mirror image of the chart in Fig. 8-15.

8-16   Block-diagram algebra

In order to make use of the properties of the diagrams of constant closed-loop gain and phase described in the preceding sections, it is necessary that the system under consideration have unity feedback. Many real systems, of course, will have feedback elements which contribute significantly to the overall loop dynamics. For these systems the block diagrams must be rearranged to have unity feedback. The simple techniques involved in effecting this rearrangement constitute the subject of block-diagram algebra. These techniques are displayed in Figs. 8-16 to 8-18. In Fig. 8-16b, $C = (R - B)G$ and $B = CH$; whence

$$\frac{C}{R} = \frac{G}{(1 + GH)}$$

as shown. The basis for the equivalence in Fig. 8-17a is the fact that

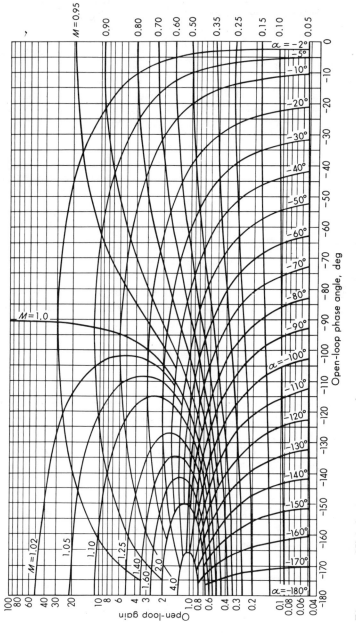

Figure 8-15 Nichols chart. M = closed-loop gain; α = closed-loop phase angle.

191

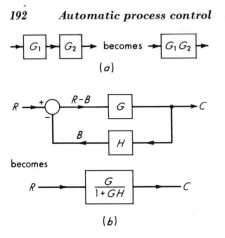

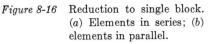

Figure 8-16   Reduction to single block.
(a) Elements in series; (b)
elements in parallel.

$(RG_1 - B)G_2 = C$, and hence $(R - B/G_1)G_1G_2 = C$.   Figure 8-17*b* follows from $(R - B)G_1G_2 = (RG_1 - BG_1)G_2$.

Figure 8-19 shows a simple example of the conversion of a nonunity
feedback system to a unity feedback system.   The determination of the
closed-loop frequency-response characteristics for this system from the
characteristics of the individual components would be carried out as
follows:

1   Determine the frequency-response characteristics of G_cGH by
graphical addition on a Bode diagram or by computation via multiplication of magnitude ratios and addition of phase angles.
2   Use the lines of constant closed-loop magnitude and phase on
Figs. 8-11 and 8-12, for example, to determine the frequency-response
characteristics of $G_cGH/(1 + G_cGH)$.
3   Correct the closed-loop characteristics from step 2 by adding in
the characteristic $1/H$, either graphically on a Bode diagram or by
computation as in step 1.

Example 8-5   In the closed-loop system of Fig. 8-19, at a frequency of 3 cycles/min, the individual components have frequency-
response characteristics as tabulated below:

	G_c	G	H
Magnitude ratio	2.8	0.15	0.80
Phase angle, deg	+4.0	−87	−32

What are the overall characteristics of the closed loop?

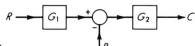

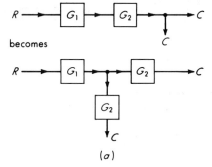

becomes

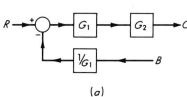

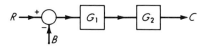

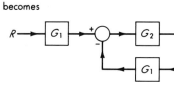

(a)

(a)

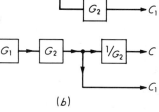

(b)

(b)

Figure 8-17   Block displacements through summing point. (*a*) Forward through summing point; (*b*) backward through summing point.

Figure 8-18   Block displacements through branch point. (*a*) Forward through branch point; (*b*) backward through branch point.

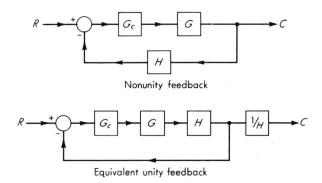

Figure 8-19   Example of conversion to unity feedback.

Solution   The open-loop gain and angle are, respectively:

$$|G_cGH| = |G_c|\,|G|\,|H| = (2.8)(0.15)(0.80) = 0.336$$
$$\underline{/G_cGH} = \underline{/G_c} + \underline{/G} + \underline{/H} = 4 - 87 - 32 = -115°$$

At these conditions on the Nichols chart (Fig. 8-15), the corresponding closed-loop gain is 0.377 and the closed-loop angle is $-98°$.

Since $\left|\dfrac{1}{H}\right| = \dfrac{1}{|H|}$

$$\left|\frac{1}{H}\right| = \frac{1}{0.80} = 1.25$$

.and

$$\underline{\bigg/\frac{1}{H}} = - \underline{/H} = -(-32) = 32°$$

Whence the overall closed-loop characteristics at this frequency are

Magnitude ratio $= (0.377)(1.25) = 0.472$

Phase angle $= -115 + 32 = -83°$

8-17   *Closed-loop frequency-response characteristics by direct vector manipulation*

In some calculations it may be more convenient to determine the closed-loop frequency-response characteristics by direct manipulation of the open-loop vectors.   For example, the determination of the frequency-response characteristics of the function $G/(1 + G_cG)$ when the characteristics of G and G_c are known involves the following steps for each frequency of interest:

1   Determine the characteristics of G_cG, which is the scalar product of two vectors, from

$$|G_cG| = |G_c|\,|G| \qquad \text{and} \qquad \underline{/G_cG} = \underline{/G_c} + \underline{/G}$$

either by direct computation or by graphical means, using the Bode diagram.

2   Add G_cG to unity vectorially.   The graphical operation is usually the simpler.   As shown in Fig. 8-20, the vectors for G_cG and

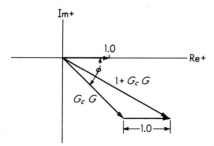

Figure 8-20 Vector addition.

unity are drawn on the complex plane, and their resultant found by setting the tail of one vector at the head of the other.

The corresponding computation is

$$|1 + G_cG| = [((|G_cG| \sin \phi + 0)^2 + (|G_cG| \cos \phi + 1)^2]^{1/2}$$

and

$$\underline{/1 + G_cG} = \tan^{-1} \frac{G_cG \sin \phi}{1 + G_cG \cos \phi}$$

3 Divide G by $1 + G_cG$ by dividing the magnitudes and subtracting the angles. Thus

$$\left| \frac{G}{1 + G_cG} \right| = \frac{|G|}{|1 + G_cG|}$$

and

$$\underline{\left/ \frac{G}{1 + G_cG} \right.} = \underline{/G} - \underline{/1 + G_cG}$$

8-18 *Damped frequency response*

As pointed out in Sec. 8-2, the roots of the characteristic equation of a feedback system [Eq. (8-5)]

$$1 + G_cG = 0 \tag{8-5}$$

determine the dynamic character of the system. The properties of this equation when the roots are purely imaginary constitute the frequency-response characteristics, which permit an immediate identification of the limiting conditions of stability.   Similarly, the properties of this equation when the roots are conjugate complex with negative real parts constitute the *damped-frequency-response* characteristics.   For many typical process systems these damped characteristics afford a direct insight into the nature of the system transient response, and as described in Chap. 9, they afford a means of designing feedback systems to a specified degree of damping and a specified speed of response.

The most convenient graphical representation of the damped frequency response is given by rewriting Eq. (8-5) in the form

$$-G_c(s) = \frac{1}{G(s)} \tag{8-57}$$

where, for the damped frequency response,

$$s = -\alpha + j\beta \tag{8-58}$$

and where, in turn, α is the damping factor, β is the damped frequency, and both α and β are real positive numbers for real systems.

According to Eq. (8-57), the plant characteristic is plotted on the inverse Nyquist diagram, and the negative controller characteristic is directly identifiable.   Instead of selecting a number of values of α and β and inserting them in G, it is usually much simpler to sketch in the damped-frequency-response characteristics from the undamped-frequency-response characteristics, using the principles of conformal mapping.

One assertion of these principles is that, if the complex quantity $s = -\alpha + j\beta$ is plotted in the complex plane as a square grid as in Fig. 8-21, any function of s will plot on the complex plane as a curvilinear square grid for the corresponding values of s.   A corollary is that the lines of constant α and constant β must be orthogonal; that is, they must intersect at right angles.

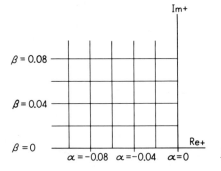

Figure 8-21   Square grid on s plane.

The procedure for sketching the damped-frequency-response characteristics for $1/G$ is shown in Fig. 8-22. First the zero-damped frequency-response locus is drawn for $s = j\omega$, and points at equal increments of ω are marked on the locus. Then tentative constant frequency lines are drawn through each of the points normal to the frequency-response locus. Next a constant damping locus is sketched inside the frequency-response locus normal to the constant frequency lines, and in such a manner that a set of curvilinear squares is formed between the two loci. The frequency lines are now extended beyond and orthogonal to the damped locus, and the various steps are repeated until a curvilinear square grid fills the left half plane.

According to Eq. (8-57), the plot in Fig. 8-22 is $-G_c(s)$, the controller characteristic. For proportional control $-G_c = -K_p$, and for any particular K_p the corresponding damping factor and damped frequency for the closed-loop system can be identified along the negative real axis. Thus, for $K_p = 1.7$, for example, $\alpha = 0.02$ and $\beta = 0.13$ in Fig. 8-22.

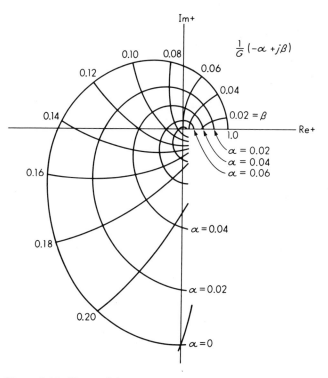

Figure 8-22   Damped-frequency-response characteristic for typical process plant.

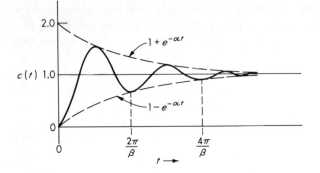

Figure 8-23   Transient response to step forcing.

In order to translate values of α and β to a transient response, we assume that the response may be approximated as a second-order response characterized by these two parameters. The damping factor α defines the decay envelope bounding the response, and the damped frequency β defines the period of oscillation as indicated in Fig. 8-23. The actual form of the transient response, of course, will depend on how the system is perturbed. How far and in what direction the initial excursion will go depends on the nature of the forcing, but the subsidence ratio of the subsequent peaks in the response and the damped period depend only on α and β. For some systems the characteristic equation may contain more than one pair of significant conjugate complex roots, with the result that there is more than one oscillatory mode. In such cases the damped-frequency-response characteristics may not give an accurate insight into the exact dynamic behavior of the system. If a precise knowledge of the transient response is required, some form of solution of the system equations must be obtained.

When the control loop is closed through a controller generating proportional plus integral action, it is not so convenient to determine graphically what damping and damped frequency will result because both G_c and G are functions of α and β. Thus

$$-G_c = -K_p\left(1 + \frac{1}{T_I s}\right) = -K_p\left[1 + \frac{1}{T_I(-\alpha + j\beta)}\right]$$

or

$$-G_c = -K_p + \frac{\alpha K_p}{T_I(\alpha^2 + \beta^2)} + j\frac{\beta K_p}{T_I(\alpha^2 + \beta^2)} \qquad (8\text{-}59)$$

For given K_p, T_I, and $G(-\alpha + j\beta)$, values of α and β must be found which satisfy Eqs. (8-5) and (8-59). Since the integrating action usually is added in modest amount to eliminate steady-state error, it contributes only slightly to the transient response, and the tedious computation implied by Eq. (8-59) is not worth the effort. The inverse problem, namely, the selection of controller parameters for specified G, α, and β, however, is quite simple, and for design purposes the damped frequency response provides uniquely useful insights.

For proportional plus derivative control or for three-mode control in which the integrating action makes a negligible contribution to the transient behavior, the analysis problem can be solved fairly readily. In this case

$$-G_c = -K_p + K_p T_D \alpha - jK_p T_D \beta \qquad (8\text{-}60)$$

and for given G, K_p, and T_D, the damping factor can be found by trial from the real part of Eq. (8-60) and the plot of $1/G$, and the damped frequency can be found by trial from the imaginary part of the equation and the plot of $1/G$.

It can be seen from the foregoing discussion that the G^{-1} plane for damped frequency response gives a clear picture of the significance of the various control modes. The conditions of damping and damped frequency accessible to the system with proportional control alone occur only on the negative real axis. Any addition of integrating action puts the control vector into the second quadrant, where frequencies are lower and where, for the same proportional control component, the damping is less.

The addition of derivative action moves the control vector into the third quadrant of the G^{-1} plane, where frequencies are greater and where, for the same proportional control component, the damping also is usually greater. It was pointed out in Chap. 6 that commercial controllers provide a compensation for excessive derivative action at high frequencies. The effect of this compensation is to limit the effective magnitude of the negative imaginary component of the control vector.

8-19 *Locus of roots*

The damped frequency response provides an estimate of the dynamic behavior of a closed-loop system from the corresponding open-loop characteristics. This estimate is based on the assumption that the closed-loop behavior is dominated by a single pair of conjugate complex roots, $s = -\alpha \pm j\beta$, which satisfy the characteristic equation of the closed loop, $G(s) = -1$. A more precise statement of this assumption is that the characteristic equation of the closed-loop system is regarded as a second-degree polynomial with complex roots having negative real parts. For many process systems, indeed for most typical process systems, this assumption is a good one, but there are also many process systems for which the characteristic equation is better regarded as being of third or higher order.

Many distributed-parameter systems and some systems with relatively large time delays, for example, as well as certain lumped-parameter systems, cannot be described reliably by characteristic equations of less than third order. For such systems it would be desirable to keep track of all the roots of the characteristic equation and to identify how the adjustable parameters of the system influence the roots.

A relatively simple graphical technique for effecting just this kind of scrutiny of the characteristic equation is the root-locus method, which was first described by Evans. In this method all the roots, or more particularly, all the important roots, of the characteristic equation of the closed-loop system are plotted on the s plane for all possible values of the open-loop steady-state gain. The resulting curves permit a direct identification of the steady-state gain required to produce a particular set of roots in the characteristic equation, or conversely, an identification of the roots at a particular gain. Since the root loci can be sketched fairly quickly for many systems, and since the location of roots gives immediate insight into the nature of the system transient response, the root-locus method has become a powerful and popular tool for the control engineer.

The construction of the root locus is based on a trial-and-error testing of likely points to satisfy the characteristic equation.

For the simple unity feedback system shown in Fig. 8-24, the closed-loop transfer function is

$$\frac{C}{R} = \frac{K_c G_c K_1 G_1}{1 + K_c G_c K_1 G_1} \tag{8-61}$$

and the characteristic equation is

$$1 + K_c G_c K_1 G_1 = 0 \tag{8-62}$$

which may be rewritten

$$1 + KG(s) = 0 \tag{8-63}$$

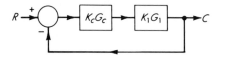

Figure 8-24 Simple unity feedback system.

where K is the adjustable frequency-independent gain K_cK_1, and $G(s)$ is the frequency-dependent part of the open-loop transfer function, G_cG_1.

The root locus of $KG(s)$ is the locus of all points in the s plane which satisfy the angle requirement of Eq. (8-63), namely,

$$\underline{/KG(s)} = \underline{/G(s)} = \pm(180° + n360°) \tag{8-64}$$

where n is zero or any integer.

Since the magnitude requirement of Eq. (8-63) is

$$|KG(s)| = 1 \tag{8-65}$$

each point on the root locus corresponds to a particular value of K, and the values of K are usually marked on the loci at convenient points. For real systems the loci describe the roots for all values of K from zero to infinity.

Typically, the open-loop transfer function for systems made up of serial arrays of simple elements, or for systems which are so representable, will be a ratio of polynomials, which in factored form is

$$KG(s) = \frac{K(s + z_1)(s + z_2)\ \cdots}{(s + p_1)(s + p_2)(s + p_3)\ \cdots} \tag{8-66}$$

where the z are the negative zeros of $G(s)$, and the p are the negative poles. The zeros are the values of s which make $G(s)$ zero, and the poles are the values of s which make $G(s)$ infinite. In the nomenclature of Eq. (8-66), if $z_1 = 1.0$, the corresponding zero is -1.0.

The factors in Eq. (8-66), in general, are vectors, and hence, from the rules for multiplying and dividing vectors,

$$\underline{/G(s)} = \underline{/s + z_1} + \underline{/s + z_2} + \cdots$$
$$- \underline{/s + p_1} - \underline{/s + p_2} - \underline{/s + p_3} - \cdots \tag{8-67}$$

which may be generalized to the statement that the angle of $G(s)$ at a particular $s = s_j$ is the difference between the sum of the angles of the vectors drawn from the zeros to s_j and the sum of angles of the vectors drawn from the poles to s_j.

A typical construction is shown in Fig. 8-25 for point s_1 and a system with a conjugate complex pair of poles with negative real parts, p_2 and p_3, a pole at the origin, $p_1 = 0$, and two negative zeros, z_1 and z_2. The point s_1 lies on the root locus if the angle of $G(s)$ at that point as given by Eq. (8-67), namely, $\theta_1 + \theta_2 - \phi_1 - \phi_2 - \phi_3$, satisfies Eq. (8-64).

In principle, the root locus must be determined by trial and error; that is, a point is chosen and then tested by the angle criterion. In practice, a shrewd identification of key points and directions through the use of a few rules as outlined below greatly simplifies the work required.

The values of the parameter K, the open-loop steady-state gain, which are to be marked on the locus, are obtained from the fact that

$$K = \left| \frac{1}{G(s)} \right| \tag{8-68}$$

where the magnitude of $G(s)$ is given by the ratio, namely, the products of the magnitudes of the vectors from the zeros to the point s divided by the products of the magnitudes of the vectors from the poles to the point s. That is,

$$|G(s)| = \frac{1}{K} = \frac{|(s + z_1)|\,|(s + z_2)| \, \cdots}{|(s + p_1)|\,|(s + p_2)|\,|(s + p_3)| \, \cdots} \tag{8-69}$$

8-20 *Construction of root loci*

Since the root loci are drawn for all values of the gain K from zero to infinity, we may regard the loci as beginning at the roots for $K = 0$ and terminating at the roots where $K = \infty$. According to Eq. (8-68), when $K = 0$, $G(s)$ must be infinite, and hence the loci originate at the poles. Similarly, when $K = \infty$, $G(s) = 0$, and hence the loci must terminate at the zeros.

The number of loci equals the number of poles, and the excess of poles over zeros identifies the number of zeros at infinity, which is, therefore, the number of loci which run off to infinity.

Since complex roots occur as conjugate pairs, the root loci are symmetrical about the real axis.

The simplest portions of the root locus to sketch are those lying on

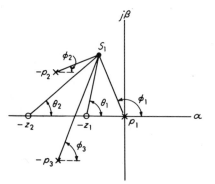

Figure 8-25   Test point for root locus.

the real axis, where the angle criterion for the loci can be satisfied only at intervals along the axis for which the total number of poles and zeros to the right of the interval is odd. This rule follows from the fact that complex poles or zeros for real systems must always occur in conjugate pairs, and hence their angle contribution for locus points on the real axis must cancel. The angle contributions of vectors drawn from zeros and poles on the real axis must be zero for locus points lying on the axis to the right of the zeros and poles, and 180° for the reverse condition.

Asymptotes for those parts of the root locus which terminate at the zeros at infinity may be located from the angles they make with the real axis and from their point of intersection on the real axis. At very large values of s, the angles contributed by all the finite zeros and poles will be essentially the same. The angles contributed by the finite zeros then will be canceled by the angles contributed by a like number of the poles, and hence the angle criterion for the root locus must be divided equally among the vectors drawn from the remaining poles. Since the number of the remaining poles is the number of zeros at infinity, we may assert that the angles of the asymptotes are given by $\pm(180 + n360)/z_i$, where z_i is the number of zeros at infinity, and n is the integer or zero in Eq. (8-64).

By algebraic manipulation of the polynomials in Eq. (8-66), together with Eq. (8-63), it can be shown that the asymptotes of the root loci must intersect at a point on the real axis given by

$$s_i = \frac{\Sigma p - \Sigma z}{n_p - n_z} \tag{8-70}$$

where p = finite pole
  z = finite zero
  n_p = number of finite poles
  n_z = number of finite zeros

The actual point at which the root locus breaks away from the real axis may be determined readily from the fact that there is no net change in angle in going from a locus point on the real axis to a locus point just slightly off the axis at the breakaway point. Figure 8-26 shows the con-

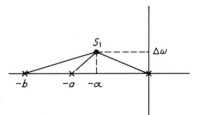

Figure 8-26 Determination of point of break-away from real axis.

struction for this determination.   If the distance from the real axis, $\Delta\omega$, is very small, the angles of the vectors drawn from the poles at 0, $-a$, and $-b$ will be equal to the tangents, and if there is no change in angle,

$$\frac{\Delta\omega}{b - \alpha} + \frac{\Delta\omega}{a - \alpha} - \frac{\Delta\omega}{\alpha} = 0$$

from which α can be computed after canceling out the $\Delta\omega$.

This rule can be generalized to the following equation if there are no complex poles or zeros:

$$\sum_1^n \frac{1}{p_n - \alpha} - \sum_1^m \frac{1}{z_m - \alpha} = 0 \tag{8-71}$$

Another conveniently located reference point on the root locus is the intersection with the imaginary axis.   This intersection occurs in conjugate pairs at the limiting condition of stability, and hence any technique for identifying the limiting condition of stability will identify the pair of intersections.   The Routh-Hurwitz criterion described in Sec. 8-9 or the graphical techniques described in Sec. 8-3 may be used for this identification.

There are a number of other rules and techniques to aid the sketching of root loci, but the ultimate procedure is a trial-and-error testing of likely points, and the power of the method lies in the ease with which a practiced engineer can sketch and manipulate the key parts of the loci. A handy tool for conducting the trial-and-error testing is the spirule designed by Evans.   This instrument is a pivoted protractor with coupled slide rule, which simultaneously determines $/G$ and K.

Example 8-6   Sketch the root locus for a flow control system which may be characterized by a pair of coupled transfer stages with respective time constants of 0.5 and 1.0 sec and which is controlled by an integral controller.   The overall steady-state gain of the open loop is 1.7.

Solution   For this system the open-loop transfer function is

$$KG = \frac{1.7}{T_I s(0.5s + 1)(s + 1)}$$

which may be written

$$KG = \frac{3.4/T_I}{s(s + 2)(s + 1)} \tag{8-72}$$

Thus

$$K = \frac{3.4}{T_I}$$

and

$$G = \frac{1}{s(s + 2)(s + 1)}$$

Since there are three finite poles, namely, at the origin, at -2, and at -1, the root locus has three branches, and since there are no finite zeros, all the branches must run off to infinity. The asymptotes for the loci at high s must lie at angles of $\pm {}^{180}\!\!/_3 = \pm 60°$ and at

$$\pm \frac{180 + 360}{3} = \pm 180°$$

i.e., on the real axis. Furthermore, according to Eq. (8-70), the pair of asymptotes at $\pm 60°$ must intersect the real axis at

$$s_i = \frac{(0 - 2 - 1) - 0}{3 - 0} = -1$$

Along the real axis one branch of the locus must lie between the pole at -1 and the origin, and another branch must lie from the pole at -2 out to minus infinity. There is no locus between -2 and -1 because the number of poles to the right of that region is even (two).

The characteristic equation for which we are plotting the roots is

$$s(s + 2)(s + 1) + K = 0$$

or

$$s^3 + 3s^2 + 2s + K = 0$$

By setting $s = j\omega$, we may compute the value of $j\omega$ at the intersection of the locus on the imaginary axis. Thus

$$-j\omega^3 - 3\omega^2 + j2\omega + K = 0$$

and from the imaginary terms,

$$\omega = \sqrt{2}$$

and from the real terms the corresponding value of K is $3\omega^2$, or 6.0.

The breakaway point from the real axis must lie between the pole at -1 and the origin because K increases in moving along the locus away from either of these poles. For a modest departure from the real axis there must be no change in net angle or no change in the net sum of the tangents, and hence

$$\frac{1}{2 - \alpha} + \frac{1}{1 - \alpha} - \frac{1}{\alpha} = 0$$

from which $-\alpha = -0.42$.

Figure 8-27 shows the root locus sketched from the foregoing information plus trial-and-error satisfaction of the angle criterion. Values of T_I ($= 3.4/K$), indicated in italics along the locus, are determined from values of K, which in turn are determined from Eq. (8-69), written for this case as

$$K = |s|\,|(s + 2)|\,|(s + 1)|$$

that is, the value of K at any point on the locus is the product of the lengths of the vectors drawn from the three poles to the point.

For typical feedback systems the dynamic behavior is dominated by a pair of conjugate complex roots with negative real parts. If the

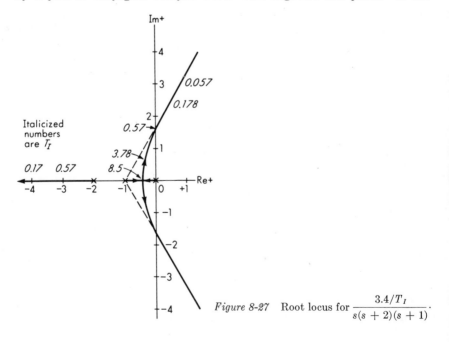

Figure 8-27   Root locus for $\dfrac{3.4/T_I}{s(s + 2)(s + 1)}$.

domination is fairly complete, the actual behavior will approximate that of a second-order system characterized by a damping ratio ζ and a damped frequency $\omega_n \sqrt{1 - \zeta^2}$ corresponding to the second-order root pair $-\zeta\omega_n \pm j\omega_n \sqrt{1 - \zeta^2}$. The point on the root locus, and hence the particular value of K, for a given damping ratio, may be found readily from the fact that the locus of constant ζ is a straight line through the origin, making an angle with the negative real axis of $\cos^{-1} \zeta$. Similarly, the locus of constant natural frequency ω_n is a circle of radius ω_n. The basis for these properties is indicated by the construction in Fig. 8-28, since the magnitude of $-\zeta\omega_n + j\omega_n \sqrt{1 - \zeta^2}$ is $[\zeta^2\omega_n{}^2 + (\omega_n \sqrt{1 - \zeta^2})^2]^{1/2} = \omega_n$.

8-21 *Phase-angle loci*

As has been emphasized, one of the key advantages of the root-locus method of analysis is the ease with which the dynamic behavior of the closed-loop system can be inferred from the open-loop poles and zeros. This easy inference disappears, however, if the open-loop transfer function cannot readily be expressed in factored form, that is, with poles and zeros clearly identified.

For example, a process system containing an appreciable time delay is properly describable only by a transfer function containing the transcendental function e^{-Ts}, which, in effect, introduces an infinite number of roots into the system characteristic equation for each value of system gain. A practical method for constructing the root locus for such a system is through use of the phase-angle loci of the open-loop-system elements.

The phase-angle-loci method for constructing root loci as devised by Yaohan Chu and described by Truxal is designed to provide an orderly procedure for complex systems where the rules for identifying the approximate positions of the root loci are not particularly helpful. In this method the loci of constant phase angle at convenient angular increments are sketched for each element in the open loop. The root loci then are

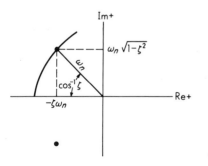

Figure 8-28 Loci of constant ζ and ω_n.

found at those intersections of the phase-angle loci which satisfy the angle criterion $\pm(180° + n360°)$.

For the first-order transfer stage the phase-angle loci are given by

$$\psi = \underline{/G(s)} = \Big/ \frac{k_1}{Ts + 1}$$

or for $s = -\alpha + j\beta$, recalling that $\psi = \tan^{-1}(\text{Im}/\text{Re})$,

$$\psi = \tan^{-1} \frac{-\beta}{1/T - \alpha}$$

Thus, at constant angles of G, hence at constant values of $\tan \psi$, the phase-angle loci are straight lines given by

$$\beta = (\tan \psi)\alpha - \frac{1}{T} \tag{8-73}$$

Some typical lines are shown in Fig. 8-29.

For the pure time delay,

$$e^{-Ts} = e^{\alpha T} e^{-j\beta T} \tag{8-74}$$

for which the angle is merely $-\beta T$ in radians, independent of α. Thus the locus for an angle of $-30°$, or $-\pi 30/180 = -\pi/6$, or -0.523 rad, is a straight line parallel to the real axis and passing through the intercept $\beta = -\text{angle}/T = +\pi/6T$. Typical loci are shown in Fig. 8-30.

Example 8-7   Sketch the root locus of a simple feedback system consisting of a proportional controller of gain K_p coupled to a process

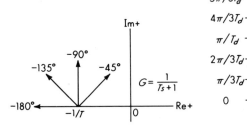

Figure 8-29   Phase-angle loci for first-order transfer stage.

Figure 8-30   Phase-angle loci for pure time delay.

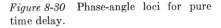

system characterized by a steady-state gain of 1.5, a first-order transfer lag of 1 min, and a distance-velocity lag, also of 1 min.

Solution   The open-loop transfer function for this system is

$$G(s) = \frac{1.5K_p e^{-s}}{s + 1} \tag{8-75}$$

and the corresponding closed-loop transfer function for unity feedback is

$$\frac{G}{1 + G} = \frac{1.5K_p e^{-s}}{s + 1 + 1.5K_p e^{-s}} \tag{8-76}$$

The root locus is found directly by superimposing phase-angle loci for $1/(s + 1)$ and for e^{-s}, as shown in Fig. 8-31. Intersections for loci which, when summed, satisfy the angle requirement for the root locus are points on the root locus. Branches of the root locus on the real axis lie between the pole at -1 and the point $-1/T_d - 1/T = -2$, and also between this point and minus unity.

Values for the loop gain $1.5K_p$ at various points on the locus are obtained by computing with Eq. (8-74) the overall open-loop magnitude ratio for the particular values of the roots given by the root locus.

Thus, on the real axis at $s = -2$, the overall magnitude, exclusive of the steady-state gain, is $|e^2/(-2 + 1)| = e^2$, and the steady-state gain is then e^{-2}, or 0.135.

At $s = -1 + j\pi/2$, the open-loop magnitude, exclusive of the steady-state gain, is

$$\left| \frac{e(e^{-j\pi/2})}{-1 + j\pi/2 + 1} \right| = \frac{2e}{\pi}$$

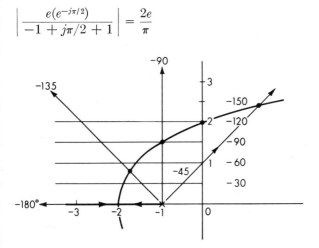

Figure 8-31   Root-locus construction, Example 8-7.

and hence the steady-state gain is $\pi/2e$, or 0.577. Note that the real part of the exponential contributes to the magnitude, but the imaginary part does not, since $|e^{-j\omega}| = 1.0$.

At the intersection of the root locus with the imaginary axis, the steady-state gain is $|j(2\pi/3) + 1| = (4\pi^2/9 + 1)^{1/2}$, or 2.32. Other gains can be computed in similar fashion.

8-22 *Transient response of loops containing time delays*

The contribution of a time delay, such as a distance-velocity lag, to the transient response of an open-loop serial array of linear elements, is easily assessed, since the only effect is a shifting of the response by an increment of time equal to the delay. If the time delay is incorporated in a feedback loop, however, the effect on the transient response of the loop cannot be predicted readily.

When the time delay is small relative to the principal time constants of one or more elements in the loop, the system characteristic equation often can be approximated by a second- or third-order polynomial, and techniques like the damped frequency response provide a good indication of the transient behavior of the system.

On the other hand, if the time delay approaches or exceeds the size of the principal time constants in the system, there may be considerable error in the inferences regarding transient responses which may be drawn from the damped frequency response. In such cases the exact transient response may be computed by expanding the delay function e^{-Ts} in an infinite series and using a large-scale automatic digital computer to ensure retaining enough terms in the series for reasonable accuracy.

An alternative procedure is to approximate the time delay by the Padé function,

$$e^{-Ts} \approx \frac{1 + a_1s + a_2s^2 + \cdots + a_ns^n}{1 + b_1s + b_2s^2 + \cdots + b_ms^m} \tag{8-77}$$

where the a and b are chosen to make the Maclaurin expansion of the ratio of the polynomials equal to the Maclaurin expansion of the time-delay function itself, up to degree $n + m$. The n and m are chosen to give the lowest practicable degree for the two polynomials. The difference between n and m is set to make the overall open-loop transfer function a proper fraction, with the degree of the numerator equal to the degree of the denominator. For typical process systems, n will exceed m by 1 or 2. Some low-degree Padé functions are listed in Table 8-2. Higher-

Table 8-2 Padé approximations for $e^{-T_d s}$

$\dfrac{2 - T_d s}{2 + T_d s}$	$\dfrac{3 - 2T_d s + \frac{1}{2}(T_d s)^2}{3 + T_d s}$
$\dfrac{4 - 3T_d s + (T_d s)^2 - \frac{1}{6}(T_d s)^3}{4 + T_d s}$	$\dfrac{10 - 6T_d s + \frac{3}{2}(T_d s)^2 - \frac{1}{6}(T_d s)^3}{10 + 4T_d s + \frac{1}{2}(T_d s)^2}$

degree approximations are given in the literature, for example by Truxal, but there is little advantage in using them because of the complexity of subsequent manipulations.

Example 8-8   The open-loop transfer function of a simple process system is closely approximated by $e^{-s}/(1 + 2s)(1 + 4s)$.   If this system is included in a feedback loop containing a controller of gain K_p, what is the simplest characteristic equation equivalent to a fourth-degree expansion of the exponential term?

Solution   The characteristic equation for the closed-loop system is

$$1 + \frac{K_p e^{-s}}{(1 + 2s)(1 + 4s)} = 0 \tag{8-78}$$

Since the degree of the denominator in the fraction is two, we should choose for the Padé approximant a ratio of polynomials in which the degree of the numerator is two greater than the degree of the denominator and for which the sum of the degrees is 4.   Thus, from Table 8-2,

$$e^{-s} \cong \frac{4 - 3s + s^2 - \frac{1}{6}s^3}{4 + s} \tag{8-79}$$

and the corresponding characteristic equation is

$$(1 + 2s)(1 + 4s)(4 + s) + K_p(4 - 3s + s^2 - \frac{1}{6}s^3) = 0$$

or

$$4(1 + K_p) + (25 - 3K_p)s + (38 + K_p)s^2 + \left(8 - \frac{K_p}{6}\right)s^3 = 0 \tag{8-80}$$

The Maclaurin expansion of e^{-s}, to give about the same reliability of approximation, would require a fourth-degree characteristic equation.

8-23   *The modified z transform*

If it is necessary to obtain an accurate estimate of the transient response of a closed-loop control system design in which there is a substantial time delay, the only practical recourse is to use some kind of numerical method.   Indeed, this is a practical recourse for complicated feedback systems without time delays because of the cumbersome character of the analytical solutions of high-order differential equations.   As discussed in Chap. 10, the high-speed analog computer can handle fairly complicated systems, but it can provide only an approximation to the pure time delay.

A powerful, yet simple, numerical method for the direct computation of the transient response of feedback systems containing time delays is that proposed by Boxer and Thaler and based on the use of the modified z transform, called the z form.

The z transform itself is described in Chap. 9 in connection with the design of systems involving the flow of intermittent rather than continuous signals.   Our treatment here of the modified z transform will present the method of Boxer and Thaler without elaboration.

There are five steps in the solution of a differential equation by this method:

1   Obtain the Laplace transform of the desired quantity.   For example, the transform of the response of a feedback control system to unit step forcing in the set point will be

$$C(s) = \frac{1}{s} \frac{G(s)}{1 + G(s)} \tag{8-81}$$

2   Rewrite this equation as a rational fraction in powers of s^{-1} by dividing both numerator and denominator through by s raised to the highest power occurring in the denominator.

3   Convert the equation in s^{-1} to the corresponding equation in powers of z^{-1}, using the modified z transforms from Table 8-3.   The basis for this transformation is the equation

$$z = e^{sT} \tag{8-82}$$

where T is an arbitrary time interval.

4   Divide the transformed equation by T, the interval of time between the points of the desired solution.   For systems with a time delay, T must be chosen so that the time delay is an integral multiple of T.

5   Divide the denominator into the numerator by synthetic division to get a series of the form

$$A_0 + A_1z^{-1} + \cdots + A_nz^{-n} + \cdots \tag{8-83}$$

The coefficient A_n, for example, is the approximate value of $c(t)$ at $t = nT$.

Example 8-9   A process system representable by a time delay of T_d min in series with a first-order transfer stage with a time constant of T_1 min is to be controlled by a proportional controller with an adjustable gain K_p.   Write out an expression for the response of this system to unit step forcing in the set point at time intervals of T_d/n_1 min, where n_1 is an integer, assuming the steady-state gain of the system is unity.

Solution   The Laplace transform of the desired response is

$$C(s) = \frac{1}{s} \frac{K_p e^{-sT_d}}{(1 + T_1s)[1 + K_p e^{-sT_d}/(1 + T_1s)]}$$

which, upon division through by s^2 and rearrangement, becomes

$$C(s) = K_p \frac{s^{-2}e^{-sT_d}}{T_1 + s^{-1}(1 + K_p e^{-sT_d})}$$

Substitute the z forms for the s terms in this expression, using Table 8-3, and eliminate the exponential terms by substituting z^{-n_1} for e^{-sT_d}

Table 8-3   z forms ($z = e^{Ts}$)

$F(s)$	$F(z)$
s^{-1}	$\dfrac{T}{2} \dfrac{1 + z^{-1}}{1 - z^{-1}}$
s^{-2}	$\dfrac{T^2}{12} \dfrac{1 + 10z^{-1} + z^{-2}}{(1 - z^{-1})^2}$
s^{-3}	$\dfrac{T^3}{2} \dfrac{z^{-1} + z^{-2}}{(1 - z^{-1})^3}$
s^{-4}	$\dfrac{T^4}{6} \dfrac{z^{-1} + 4z^{-2} + z^{-2}}{(1 - z^{-1})^4} - \dfrac{T^4}{720}$
s^{-5}	$\dfrac{T^5}{24} \dfrac{z^{-1} + 11z^{-2} + 11z^{-3} + z^{-4}}{(1 - z^{-1})^5}$

since $e^{-n_1 sT} = z^{-n_1}$, to get

$$C(z) = K_p \frac{T^2}{12} \frac{1 + 10z^{-1} + z^{-2}}{(1 - z^{-1})^2} \frac{z^{-n_1}}{T_1 + \frac{T}{2}\frac{1 + z^{-1}}{1 - z^{-1}}(1 + K_p z^{-n_1})}$$

which, upon division by T and expansion of numerator and denominator, is

$$\frac{C(z)}{T} = \frac{K_p T}{6} \frac{z^{-n_1} + 10z^{-1-n} + z^{-2-n}}{2T_1 + T - 4T_1 z^{-1} + (2T_1 - T)z^{-2} + TK_p z^{-n_1} - TK_p z^{-n_1 - 2}}$$

If the division indicated by the right-hand side of this equation is carried out, the resulting coefficients on the successive z terms are the values of the response $c(t)$ at times nT.

As a specific example, let $T_d = 1$ min, $T_1 = 4$ min, $T = \frac{1}{2}$; hence $n_1 = 2$, and $K_p = 2.0$. The equation arranged in ascending powers of z^{-1} after insertion of the numerical values is

$$\frac{C(z)}{T} = \frac{0.0196z^{-2} + 0.196z^{-3} + 0.0196z^{-4}}{1.0 - 1.88z^{-1} + z^{-2} - 0.118z^{-4}}$$

and the synthetic division is

$$
\begin{array}{r}
0.0196z^{-2} + 0.233z^{-3} + \cdots \\
1.0 - 1.88z^{-1} + z^{-2} + 0 - 0.118z^{-4} \overline{\big)\, 0.0196z^{-2} + 0.196z^{-3} + 0.0196z^{-4}} \\
0.0196z^{-2} - 0.037z^{-3} + 0.0196z^{-4} \\
|\; 0 - 0.00232z^{-6} \\
\hline
+ 0.233z^{-3} + 0 + 0 \\
- 0.00232z^{-6} \\
\cdots \cdots \cdots
\end{array}
$$

The result of the division out to z^{-6} is

$$0.0196z^{-2} + 0.233z^{-3} + 0.438z^{-4} + 0.592z^{-5} + 0.680z^{-6}$$

Hence the response over time may be tabulated as:

	$n = 0$	$n = 1$	$n = 2$	$n = 3$	$n = 4$	$n = 5$	$n = 6$
$t = nT$, min	0	0.5	1.0	1.5	2.0	2.5	3.0
$c(t)$	0	0	0.196	0.233	0.438	0.592	0.680

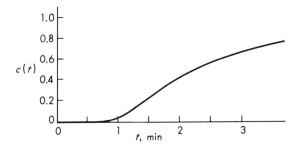

Figure 8-32   Step response of system in Example 8-9.

This system clearly is highly damped, as shown by the sketch of the response in Fig. 8-32.

The method of Boxer and Thaler is generally useful for solving ordinary differential equations either with or without constant coefficients, and it can be used for certain types of nonlinear differential equations. In general, the accuracy of the method increases with smaller values of the sampling time interval T.

Problems

8-1   A simple feedback control system consists of a proportional controller with gain K_p coupled to a process characterized by time constants of 2 and 10 sec and a steady-state gain of 14.2.   The controlled variable is sensed by an element with a time constant of 10 sec and a time delay of 4 sec; and the reference signal is fed to the controller summer through a first-order pneumatic transmitter with a time constant of 1 sec.

  a. Sketch a block diagram for this system.

  b. Write the transfer function relating the controlled variable C to the reference R.

  c. Write the transfer function relating the sensor output C_1 to the set point R.

8-2   Sketch the frequency-response characteristics of the process in Prob. 8-1, exclusive of the steady-state gain, on Bode, Nyquist, and inverse Nyquist diagrams.

8-3   Sketch the frequency-response characteristics $(C/R)(j\omega)$ of the closed-loop system of Prob. 8-1 on Bode, Nyquist, inverse Nyquist, and Nichols diagrams.

8-4   A proportional plus integral controller is used to control a system in which all other elements in the loop together have the characteristics of a 10-sec time delay in series with two first-order transfer stages of 20- and 40-sec time constants.   If the integral time is set equal to the ultimate period for proportional control alone, what are the proportional gain, the integral time, and the critical frequency at the limiting condition of stability? Solve this problem by means of the inverse Nyquist diagram.

8-5 Repeat Prob. 8-4 analytically by manipulating the system characteristic equation. Identify all assumptions.

8-6 Solve Prob. 8-4 by means of the Routh-Hurwitz criterion for stability. Identify all assumptions.

8-7 A temperature-controlled polymerization process is estimated to have a transfer function

$$G = \frac{k}{(s - 40)(s + 80)(s + 100)}$$

Show by means of the Routh-Hurwitz criterion that two conditions of controller parameters define upper and lower bounds on the stability of the feedback system incorporating this process. What is the significance of the positive pole in the open-loop process?

8-8 Sketch the locus of roots for the feedback system in Prob. 8-7.

8-9 A simple process with dynamic characteristics equivalent to two first-order elements with time constants of 8 min coupled in series is to be connected to a measuring element which acts like a 2-min time delay and a 4-min time-constant first-order lag controlled by a proportional controller. Sketch the locus of roots for this system.

8-10 Estimate the true behavior of the process output of the feedback system of Prob. 8-9 when the reference signal to the controller is step-forced a unit amount. Assume the controller proportional gain is half the ultimate proportional gain.

nine
design of simple control systems

The design of simple process control systems frequently involves little more than the specification of the types of measuring instruments, control valves, and controllers that must be deployed about a given process unit. This simplicity of problem often results from the fact that the process design is fixed, and not accessible to any substantial revision by the control engineer, and further, from the fact that the process, by the very nature of its development and design, is inherently quite stable and easy to control. In this chapter we focus our attention on the problem of selecting controller characteristics which will ensure acceptable operating performance for specified simple process systems. Both frequency-response characterization and the transient response are used in making the selection.

9-1   Stability

Three properties of the dynamic behavior of a process control system determine the nature of the controller characteristics required for adequate control. These properties are the dynamic stability, the accuracy of control, and the speed of response.

It is almost axiomatic that the controlled system be stable, since instability is the antithesis of control. At the same time, excessive stability for most process control systems is undesirable because sluggishness of response is a concomitant of excessive stability. The following two rules in terms of frequency-response characterization afford a practical compromise between sensitivity and sluggishness, and when applied to most process control systems, the resulting design has a transient response which is slightly underdamped.

RULE 1   For good stable control the open-loop gain margin should lie between 2.0 and 2.5 (6.0 to 8.0 db).

RULE 2   Similarly, the open-loop phase margin should lie between 45 and 60°.

In the simple control system of Fig. 9-1 the open-loop frequency-response characteristics are given by $G_c(j\omega)G(j\omega)$, where G_c is the transfer function of the control-function generator and G is the lumped transfer function of all the process elements and other units in the loop. The specific characteristics are the magnitude ratio $|G_c(j\omega)G(j\omega)|$ and the phase angle $\underline{/G_c(j\omega)G(j\omega)}$.

Since our concern here is with the stability of the system, the open-loop characteristics are the same whether we are considering the servo problem or the regulator problem.

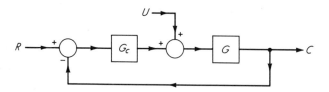

Figure 9-1 Simple control system.

Typical frequency-response characteristics for this system are shown in Fig. 9-2. For this system the controller is a proportional controller with a gain K_p of approximately 3.2 (10 db), or a proportional band of $100/3.2 = 31$ percent. The gain margin of $1/0.44$, or 2.26 (7 db), is the margin of safety in the magnitude ratio at the critical frequency ω_0. This critical frequency is the frequency at phase crossover, which is the point at which the overall phase angle of the entire open-loop system first reaches $-360°$. On the Bode diagram we plot only $G_c(j\omega)G(j\omega)$, and the shift of $180°$, which occurs at the set-point summer, is not shown. Thus phase crossover obtains on the diagram at an overall phase angle of $-180°$.

The phase margin of approximately 60° is the margin of safety in the phase angle at the condition of gain crossover, which is the point at which the overall magnitude ratio first reaches zero decibels.

Adherence to these two rules for adequate margins in phase and gain will ensure a stable control system for all typical process systems. The two rules are generally mutually complementary rather than mutually exclusive. When they are at odds, the rule to invoke will depend on how conservative the design should be. It is important to remember that these rules will ensure only that the control system will be reasonably stable. They have no direct bearing on either the accuracy of control or on the speed of response of the system.

As a very rough approximation, it may be expected that the systems designed for stability, using these margin rules, will have transient responses which damp out with subsidence ratios of about 3:1 at frequencies lying between the frequencies at the two crossover points.

If it is necessary to be sure that the controlled system will not undergo excessive overshoots or undershoots, it may be desirable to design the system for a particular peak in the closed-loop magnitude ratio.

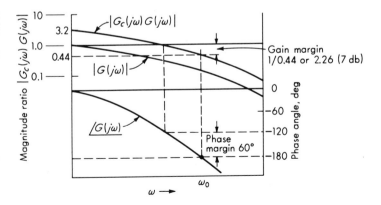

Figure 9-2 Open-loop frequency-response characteristics.

RULE 3   The peak value of the closed-loop magnitude ratio should not exceed 1.20 to 1.30.

For most process systems it will be found that the maximum over-shoot (expressed as total fractional response) that can occur in response to step forcing will approximate the maximum closed-loop magnitude ratio when the latter is around 1.20.   In order to make the necessary adjust-ment in controller gain to produce a particular closed-loop magnitude ratio, a simple proportioning is applied to either the Nyquist diagram with constant-M circles or to the Nichols chart.   The construction on the Nyquist diagram is shown in Fig. 9-3, where the open-loop frequency-response characteristics, including all controller and plant elements, is given by $G(j\omega)$ for a unity feedback system.   A vector is drawn from the origin to the likely point on the particular constant closed-loop magnitude circle, in this case the $M = 1.2$ circle, where the $G(j\omega)$ locus would just be tangent to the M circle if G were multiplied by the appropriate constant. The scaling-up factor for the controller gain, then, is simply $(a + b)/a$, and the necessary controller gain, if K_p is the controller gain in $G(j\omega)$, is $K_p[(a + b)/a]$.

The corresponding construction on the Nichols chart is done most simply by using a pair of charts, one of which is a transparent overlay. The locus of the open-loop frequency-response characteristics, including the controller with K_p equal to unity, is drawn on one chart, and the over-lay is placed on this chart but is shifted downward at constant phase angle until the drawn curve is just tangent to the desired closed-loop magnitude ratio on the overlay.   The net vertical displacement of the two charts is the required controller gain.

Both of the graphical constructions described above apply as given only to systems with unity feedback.   If the system is being designed to handle load changes occurring at intermediate points in the control loop, the feedback will not be unity.   For these cases it is necessary to use

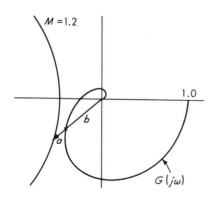

Figure 9-3   Construction for peak in closed-loop magnitude ratio.

block-diagram algebra as in Sec. 8-16 to convert the systems to equivalent loops having unity feedback, thereby retaining the convenience of either the Nichols chart or the M circles on the Nyquist diagram in obtaining the corresponding closed-loop characteristics.

9-2 Accuracy

For process control systems the matter of accuracy of control has to do primarily with the steady-state error.   In the design of servomechanisms, dynamic error is an important measure of performance, but where this kind of design is pertinent to process systems, as in the case of program control, it is usually sufficient to treat accuracy in terms of the steady-state error.   In program control the set point of the controller is varied in a predetermined way, but usually quite slowly.

The offset, or steady-state, error which will occur in the system of Fig. 9-1 may be found by applying the final-value theorem for the Laplace transformation [Eq. (3-58)] as in Sec. 8-4.   For a step load change equivalent to A in the disturbance u, that is, which would result in a change in c of A in the absence of any corrective action,

$$c_s = \lim_{s \to 0} \frac{A}{1 + G_c} \qquad (8\text{-}17)$$

where c_s is the actual steady-state deviation, or offset.

If the only control mode used in the system is proportional control, the offset is

$$c_s = \frac{A}{1 + K_p} \qquad (9\text{-}1)$$

Thus a proportional gain of 9.0 will tolerate a steady-state error amounting to 10 percent of the disturbance.   Usually, process disturbances will be kept relatively small by the nature of the design of the system, but for most systems it is prudent to avoid offsets in excess of approximately 5 percent of the disturbance.   This rule requires that additional controlling action beyond proportional control be employed if the stability requirements of the system make the proportional gain less than 19.0.

Either integrating action or derivative action may be added to proportional control to reduce the steady-state error.   Integrating action eliminates the offset altogether, since the denominator of Eq. (8-17) becomes infinite for $G_c = K_p(1 + 1/T_I s)$.

The addition of derivative action reduces the offset by increasing the stability of the system, thereby permitting the use of higher proportional gains and correspondingly smaller offsets. Commercially available controllers most usually provide either proportional plus integral control or three-mode control rather than proportional plus derivative control. Accordingly, we treat the problem of improving system accuracy by adding automatic reset (integral action).

RULE 4   If the proportional gain required for good stable control as fixed by Rules 1 and 2 is less than 20 (proportional band greater than 5 percent), add integral action to the control-function generator. Set the integral time approximately to $10/\omega_0$, that is,

$$T_I = \frac{10}{\omega_0} \tag{9-2}$$

where T_I is the integral time in minutes and ω_0 is critical frequency (frequency at phase crossover) in radians per minute.

The addition of integral action is destabilizing; hence the amount of integration that is added should be the maximum possible without destabilizing the system. For this reason the specification of Eq. (9-2) usually is made so that the contribution of the integrating action to the overall phase angle at or near the critical frequency will be small. The equation itself is derived directly from the properties of the straight-line approximation to the phase angle of proportional plus integral control.

If a more rapid integrating action (small integral time) is desired to avoid prolonged offset, the proportional gain must be reduced to maintain the same degree of stability.

9-3   Speed of response

A control system may have adequate stability and accuracy but be unsatisfactory because the responses to disturbances, though properly underdamped, are too sluggish. Since the speed of response, or more particularly, the frequency of the damped oscillations in the response, is related to the critical frequency, it is possible to increase the speed of response by adding the derivative mode to the control action.

RULE 5   If the stable response of the control system to disturbances is sluggish, add derivative action with the lead time set to

$$T_D = \frac{1}{\omega_0} \tag{9-3}$$

This specification is somewhat arbitrary inasmuch as the principal effect of the differentiating action is to add $+90°$ to the overall open-loop phase angle. For ideal three-mode control this addition obtains for all frequencies above $10/T_D$. Whether a substantial increase in response speed can result depends on the slope of the phase curve at phase crossover, since the increase in ω_0 with addition of derivative action is greater, the flatter the slope.

The addition of derivative action is advantageous if the result is a large increase in the critical frequency. For systems containing large dead times or time delays, however, the increase in the critical frequency often is too small to warrant the addition. A commonly used criterion for determining when derivative action should be added is that the critical frequency should increase by a factor of at least 2 or 3. It can be shown readily that for systems dominated by a single time delay, the increase in frequency is as small as 25 percent.

Example 9-1 A process plant may be characterized approximately by a time delay of 8 sec coupled to a second-order transfer lag with time constants of 10 and 20 sec. This plant is to be controlled with a multiple-mode controller set to a gain margin of 2.5. Integral action is to be added only if the steady-state error for reference changes is greater than 5 percent. Furthermore, the addition of the integration must not change the critical frequency of the system when the integral phase contribution is represented by the straight-line approximations. Derivative action is to be added only if the critical frequency can be more than doubled. What controller characteristics are required for this system?

Solution The open-loop frequency-response characteristics of the plant are for phase angle, $\tan^{-1} 10\omega + \tan^{-1} 20\omega + 8\omega \, (180/\pi)$, where ω is the sinusoidal signal frequency in radians per second, and for magnitude ratio overall, $1/(1 + 100\omega^2)^{1/2} \, (1 + 400\omega^2)^{1/2}$. These quantities are tabulated below, with magnitude ratio expressed in decibels. A Bode plot for this system is shown in Fig. 9-4.

Frequency, rad/sec	Magnitude, db	Phase angle, deg
0.01	−0.2	−22
0.02	−0.8	−42
0.04	−2.7	−78
0.06	−5.7	−107
0.08	−7.3	−132
0.10	−10.0	−154
0.20	−19.3	−230
0.40	−30.4	−340

From the diagram we find the critical frequency at $G = -180°$ to be $\omega_0 = 0.135$, and the corresponding magnitude ratio is -13.5 db, or 0.211. Thus $K_{p_0} = 1/0.211$, or 4.74, and for a gain margin of 2.5, $K_p = 4.74/2.5$, or 1.9. The steady-state error which this proportional control would tolerate for reference input changes is $100/(1 + 1.9) = 34.5$ percent; hence integral action must be added.

According to Rule 4, the integral time should be

$$T_I = \frac{10}{\omega_0} = \frac{10}{0.135} = 74.1 \text{ sec}$$

or 1.23 min, corresponding to a reset rate of $1/1.23 = 0.8$ repeat per minute.

It can be seen from the diagram that the slope of the phase curve for doubling the frequency from 0.1 to 0.2 rad/sec is less than 80°; hence it is probably advantageous to add derivative action to the controller. According to Rule 4, the lead time should be set to

$$T_D = \frac{1}{\omega_0} = \frac{1}{0.135} = 7.41 \text{ sec}$$

9-4   *Damped frequency response*

The design of a single-loop control system to give a particular damping and damped frequency in the transient response can be undertaken directly by means of the damped frequency response.

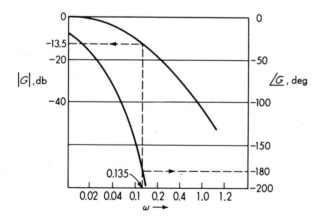

Figure 9-4   Bode diagram for $G = e^{-8s}/(1 + 10s)(1 + 20s)$.

Example 9-2 The dynamics of a process system can be represented by a general plant characteristic consisting of a pure time delay of 8 sec, coupled to a first-order transfer lag with a time constant of 4 sec and a second-order element for which the natural frequency is 0.2 rad/sec and the damping ratio is 0.8. What controller properties would be required to control this system so that the transient responses would be characterized by a damping factor of 0.04 and a damped frequency of 0.2 rad/sec?

Solution The transfer function for this process system is

$$G = \frac{e^{-8s}}{(1 + 4s)(25s^2 + 8s + 1)} \tag{9-4}$$

and the zero-damped frequency-response characteristics are given as the inverse Nyquist plot in Fig. 9-5 by the outermost locus. The damped-

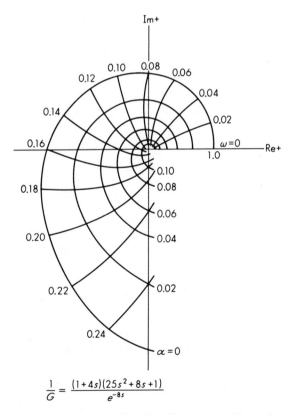

$$\frac{1}{G} = \frac{(1 + 4s)(25s^2 + 8s + 1)}{e^{-8s}}$$

Figure 9-5 Inverse Nyquist diagram for Example 9-2.

frequency-response characteristics are given by the grid of curvilinear squares within the zero-damping locus. Each locus orthogonal to the zero-damping locus corresponds to a particular damped frequency, and the remaining curves correspond to particular damping factors. These two sets of loci are obtained simply by sketching in curvilinear squares from fixed increments of frequency on the zero-damped locus. A more accurate procedure would be to compute points on the grid by substituting $s = -\alpha + j\beta$ into the reciprocal of Eq. (9-4) and inserting particular values of α and β in the real and imaginary parts.

We assume, for the purposes of this illustration, that the amount of integrating action provided in the controller will not appreciably affect the transient behavior, and further, that ideal proportional plus derivative control may be used. The controller transfer function, therefore, is

$$G_c = K_p(1 + T_D s) \tag{9-5}$$

where K_p is the proportional gain, and T_D is the derivative time.

In terms of the damped frequency response,

$$G_c = K_p[1 + T_D(-\alpha + j\beta)]$$

or

$$\mathrm{Re}\, G_c = K_p - \alpha T_D K_p \tag{9-6}$$

and

$$\mathrm{Im}\, G_c = \beta T_D K_p \tag{9-7}$$

From Fig. 9-5, at $\alpha = 0.04$ and $\beta = 0.2$, the real coordinate of $1/G$ is -0.6 and the imaginary coordinate is -0.9. According to the characteristic equation of the closed-loop system,

$$G_c = -\frac{1}{G}$$

and therefore the real part of G_c is 0.6 and the imaginary part is 0.9. Then, from Eq. (9-7),

$$K_p - 0.04 T_D K_p = 0.6$$

and simultaneous solution gives $K_p = 0.62$ and $T_D = 7.3$ sec.

According to Fig. 9-5, it should be possible to attain damped frequencies even higher than the 0.2 rad/sec of the foregoing example by increasing the derivative time. As a matter of practice, and as pointed out in Sec. 6-10, it is necessary to limit the response of derivative control action at high frequencies. This limitation, or compensation, has the effect of making certain regions of the third quadrant in the polar diagram inaccessible to a control system design. Problem 9-2 involves an appraisal of this effect.

9-5   Root-locus method

The use of the damped frequency response for the design of feedback control systems focuses attention on a single pair of conjugate complex roots of the characteristic equation of the system. A logical extension of this approach would be to scrutinize all the important roots of the characteristic equation as in the root-locus method.

This method permits the designer to adjust the system parameters to produce a particular set of roots, which correspond to a particular dynamic behavior. In principle, all the roots of the characteristic equation are fixed and identified with this method, and hence any particular transient response can be computed from the general-solution expression

$$y = A_1 e^{s_1 t} + A_2 e^{s_2 t} + \cdots \tag{9-8}$$

where the A's depend on the initial conditions, and the s's are the roots. In practice, the root-locus method derives its usefulness from the ease with which the designer can manipulate the roots and relate them to the system response. For systems with open-loop transfer functions expressed in factored form, i.e., as in Eq. (8-66),

$$KG(s) = K \frac{(s + z_1)(s + z_2) \cdots}{(s + p_1)(s + p_2)(s + p_3) \cdots} \tag{8-66}$$

the root loci can be sketched readily as described in Sec. 8-20. Furthermore, the amplitudes A on the exponential terms in Eq. (9-8) can be determined by simple graphical constructions on the root-locus plot. These constructions are based on Eq. (8-45),

$$A_j = \lim_{s \to -s_j} \frac{p(s)(s + s_j)}{q(s)} \tag{8-45}$$

and the fact that, when $p(s)$ and $q(s)$ are in factored form, the factors are vectors on the s plane, which are immediately identifiable when s is set equal to $-s_j$ after canceling out the factor $s + s_j$ from $q(s)$. With experience the designer can gauge quickly the effects of the poles and zeros of the open-loop characteristics, both on the roots of the closed-loop characteristic equation and on the amplitude terms in the response equation.

For systems in which the open-loop transfer functions cannot be expressed in factored form, for example, in systems with distributed parameters or with time delays, the root-locus method offers only marginal advantage, and then only for the engineer experienced in its use.

9-6   Ziegler-Nichols method

A simple method for selecting optimum controller settings for conventional controllers on typical single-loop process control systems was proposed by Ziegler and Nichols in 1942 as a result of empirical studies of a wide variety of systems. This method uses the step response of the open-loop system, exclusive of controller, to characterize the system dynamics. In descriptions of the Ziegler-Nichols method, the step response is often referred to as the *reaction curve*, or *signature curve*, of the process. The characterizing parameters are the apparent dead time T_d and the maximum slope S_m as shown in Fig. 9-6.

The maximum slope is the slope at the point of inflection, and the dead time is fixed by the intercept of the maximum-slope line on the time axis. The use of these parameters is approximately equivalent to representing the system by a first-order time lag plus a pure time delay.

For proportional control only,

$$K_p = \frac{1}{S_m T_d} \tag{9-9}$$

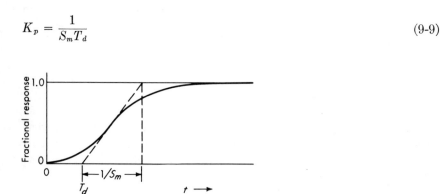

Figure 9-6   Signature curve for Ziegler-Nichols method.

and for proportional plus integral control,

$$K_p = \frac{0.9}{S_m T_d} \tag{9-10}$$

$$T_I = \frac{T_d}{0.3} \tag{9-11}$$

where T_I is the integral time.

For three-mode controllers in which the rate-compensating constant a is about 0.05 [Eq. (6-21)],

$$K_p = \frac{1.2}{S_m T_d} \tag{9-12}$$

$$T_I = 2T_d \tag{9-13}$$

and

$$T_D = \frac{T_d}{2} \tag{9-14}$$

where T_D is the derivative time.

9-7 *Empirical method based on ultimate gain and frequency*

Ziegler and Nichols also proposed that controllers could be adjusted on the basis of the ultimate proportional gain and the ultimate, or critical, frequency of the control system. This method is similar to the use of open-loop frequency-response characteristics, except that the limiting condition of stability is determined directly. The procedure is to perturb the set point with the system on proportional control alone, starting with a low proportional gain and increasing the gain until the system first cycles steadily. The proportional gain at this condition is the ultimate proportional gain K_{p_0}, and the frequency of the oscillation is the ultimate, or critical, frequency ω_0 rad/unit time, or f_0 cycles/unit time.

In terms of these two parameters, the recommended controller settings for good stable control are, for proportional control alone,

$$K_p = 0.5K_{p_0} \tag{9-15}$$

for proportional plus integral,

$$K_p = 0.45K_{p_0} \tag{9-16}$$

$$T_I = \frac{1}{1.2f_0} \tag{9-17}$$

and for three-mode control of the same type as used in the Ziegler and Nichols studies,

$$K_p = 0.6K_{p_0} \tag{9-18}$$

$$T_I = \frac{1}{2f_0} \tag{9-19}$$

$$T_D = \frac{1}{8f_0} \tag{9-20}$$

These specifications imply the following relationships between the ultimate properties and signature-curve constants:

$$T_d = \frac{1}{4f_0} \tag{9-21}$$

$$S_m = \frac{8f_0}{K_{p_0}} \tag{9-22}$$

Both of the methods of Ziegler and Nichols are applicable only to process systems which already exist and which may be step-forced while in operation. Both are concerned with a very narrow aspect of control system design, namely, the identification of the optimum settings for conventional controllers. The method based on ultimate proportional band and critical frequency is a common method of adjusting controllers in the field, the so-called "field tuning" of installed controllers.

9-8   Discontinuous systems

The control systems we have described up to this point have been continuous systems. There are two important kinds of systems in which there are discontinuities in the signals flowing in the system. One is the large class of systems controlled by on-off, or multiple-position, controllers, and the other is the class of systems called sampled-data control systems.

As was pointed out in Chap. 6, the on-off controller may be regarded as the limiting case of a proportional controller with a very high gain.

Hence systems for which a stable control can be attained by means of proportional control with K_p equal to 50 or higher, for example, can be controlled adequately by an on-off controller. These systems, typically, are regulator systems in which the process dynamics are dominated by a single first-order transfer stage or two stages in series with time constants much larger than those of the measuring and controlling instrumentation hardware. The open-loop frequency-response characteristics of such systems have great signal attenuation at the frequencies necessary to produce 180° phase lag, and consequently, a correspondingly great amplification is tolerable in the controller.

A familiar example of a system which is quite effectively controllable by an on-off controller is the household heating system, a thermal system with a large capacitance and subjected to modest disturbances.

As regulators with small disturbances, these large-capacitance systems are excellently controllable. As servomechanisms, on the other hand, they are poorly controllable, and their response to set-point changes is excessively sluggish.

9-9   Sampled-data control systems

In sampled-data control systems the flow of signals at some point or points in the system is in the form of discrete signals instead of a continuous signal. These intermittent, discrete signals usually arise from an orderly sampling of one or more variables in the system; hence the name.

A simple example of a manually controlled sampled-data system is a fractionating column which is checked and adjusted by a human operator at regular intervals of, say, 30 min. In the corresponding automatically controlled case, the overhead-stream composition might be measured automatically but intermittently by a spectrometer, working on samples withdrawn at 20-min intervals.

Sampled-data systems arise of necessity when continuous monitoring of the principal controlled process variable is not possible or not desirable. The measurement of chemical composition, for example, often cannot be done conveniently by a continuous analyzer but can be done intermittently in a cycle of, say, 10 to 20 min. Furthermore, composition-measuring instruments may be expensive, and the sharing of them by more than one control system through alternating cycles affords a desirable economy of operation.

Sampled-data control systems typically contain, in addition to conventional continuous-process elements, one or more samplers, one or more hold circuits, and a controller, which either may be continuous in operation or may be a discrete-type controller, receiving and generating digital signals. Hold, or holding, circuits are essential in sampled-data control systems to smooth out the signals from the samplers. As their name implies, they hold the sampled signal at its full magnitude at the time of sampling over the interval of time between samplings. Figure 9-7 shows a simple sampled-data control system with a single sampler and a continuous controller.

9-10 Sampler

The holding-circuit element is designated by the transfer function H, and the sampler is designated by a coupled pair of chopper bars separated by an element with transfer function B. In typical process systems the transfer function B is a pure time delay

$$B = Ke^{-Ts} \qquad (9\text{-}23)$$

where K is a calibration constant for the measuring instrument, and T is the sampling interval.

The function of the first sampler is to convert the input signal $c(t)$ from a continuous signal to a train of uniformly spaced pulses. If the sampling time, or duration of the pulse, is short compared with the sampling interval, as is usually the case, the pulses may be regarded as impulses, with heights equal to the input magnitudes at the sampling instants of time. Figure 9-8 shows a typical input and the corresponding output from the chopper bar.

The output pulses may be taken to be the product of a unit impulse and the value of the input at each sampling instant. Expressed as an infinite series, the succession of unit impulses at times T, $2T$, . . . is

$$\sum_{n=0}^{\infty} u_0(t - nT)$$

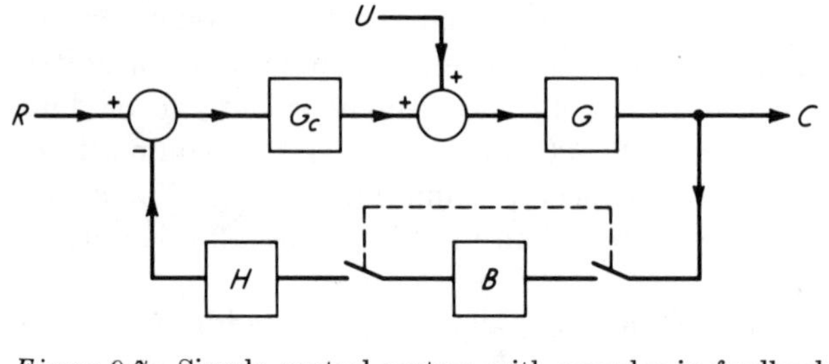

Figure 9-7 Simple control system with sampler in feedback circuit.

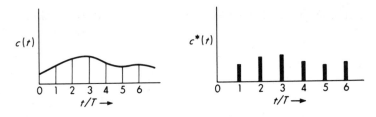

Figure 9-8   Sampler input and output.

where $u_0(t)$ is the unit impulse at $t = 0$, and $u_0(t - T)$ is the unit impulse at $t = T$, that is, translated one sampling period in time, etc.   Thus

$$c^*(t) = \sum_{n=0}^{\infty} c(nT)u_0(t - nT) \tag{9-24}$$

where the asterisk indicates the sampled function, and $c(nT)$ is the value of the input at $t = nT$.   The Laplace transformation of this equation is, simply,

$$C^*(s) = \sum_{n=0}^{\infty} c(nT)e^{-nTs} \tag{9-25}$$

since the transform of the unit impulse is unity, and translation in time of nT is given by multiplication by e^{-nTs}.

9-11   Hold element

The simplest hold-circuit element is the zero-order hold, or clamper, which has the characteristics shown in Fig. 9-9.   Over each sampling interval T the magnitude is constant at the value of the input pulse at the start of the interval.

Since the output consists of a positive step of magnitude A, followed

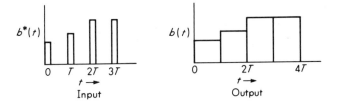

Figure 9-9   Hold-element input and output.

by a negative step of the same magnitude T sec later, the response transform is

$$A \left(\frac{1}{s} - \frac{e^{-Ts}}{s} \right)$$

where A is the input-pulse magnitude and also the input transform. The transfer function of the hold, then, is

$$H(s) = \frac{1 - e^{-Ts}}{s} \qquad (9\text{-}26)$$

9-12   z transform

The treatment of sampled-data control systems may be simplified by the use of the z transform. The variable z is defined by

$$z = e^{sT} \qquad (9\text{-}27)$$

where T is the sampling interval.
According to this definition,

$$s = \frac{1}{T} \ln z \qquad (9\text{-}28)$$

and the z transformation, in principle, is effected by making this substitution for s in a Laplace-transformed expression. Thus, for the quantity $C(s)$, the z transform is $C[(1/T) \ln z]$, which in common usage is designated simply $C(z)$.

Example 9-3   Find the z transform of a unit step.

Solution   The Laplace transform of a unit step identified at successive sampling intervals T is

$$U^*(s) = 1 + e^{-Ts} + e^{-2Ts} + \cdots \qquad (9\text{-}29)$$

In terms of z, this equation becomes

$$U(z) = 1 + \frac{1}{z} + \frac{1}{z^2} + \cdots \qquad (9\text{-}30)$$

and in closed form, by summing the series for $z > 1.0$,

$$U(z) = \frac{z}{z - 1} \qquad (9\text{-}31)$$

A short list of z transforms with corresponding Laplace transforms and time functions is given in Table 9-1.

The use of this table is similar to the use of a table of Laplace transforms in that the temporal response of a system, at least at the sampling instants, can be determined by inspection when the z transform for the response is known in forms given by the table. Some convenience in manipulation which obtains for the Laplace transform is lacking for the z transform. In particular, whereas the overall transfer function for two elements in series is given by the product of the respective transfer functions of the individual elements, the corresponding overall pulse transfer function is *not* given by the product of the respective pulse transfer functions of the individual elements unless the two elements are separated by a sampler.

In the system of tandem elements shown in Fig. 9-10, a sampler separates the two elements, and the overall z transfer function is given

Table 9-1 *z transforms*

$f(t)$	$F(s)$	$F(z)$
$u_0(t)$ (unit impulse at $t = 0$)	1	1
$u_0(t - nT)$ (unit impulse at $t = nT$)	e^{-nTs}	z^{-n}
$u(t)$ (unit step)	s^{-1}	$\dfrac{1}{z - 1}$
At	$\dfrac{A}{s^2}$	$\dfrac{ATz}{(z - 1)^2}$
e^{-at}	$\dfrac{1}{s + a}$	$\dfrac{z}{z - e^{-aT}}$
$\sin bt$	$\dfrac{b}{s^2 + b^2}$	$\dfrac{z \sin bT}{z^2 - 2z \cos bT + 1}$
$e^{t/T} \sin bt$	$\dfrac{b}{(s - 1/T)^2 + b^2}$	$\dfrac{ze \sin bT}{z^2 - 2ez \cos bT + e^2}$
$e^{-at}f(t)$	$F(s + a)$	$F(e^{aT}z)$

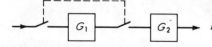

Figure 9-10   Series elements separated by sampler.

by the product of the individual z transfer functions, namely, $G_1(z)G_2(z)$. This case is entirely analogous to the case of continuous signal flow through series elements where the overall transfer function is $G_1(s)G_2(s)$. If there is no sampler between the elements, the output from G_2 will depend not only on the inputs to G_2 at the sampling instants, but also on the inputs during the intervals between the sampling instants.   It is for this reason that the z transforms are not simply multiplicative.

Example 9-4   Write the overall pulse transfer function or z transfer function for a coupled pair of first-order transfer stages with respective time constants of 1 and 0.5 min.

Solution   The overall transfer function for this system is

$$G(s) = \frac{2}{(1 + s)(2 + s)} \tag{9-32}$$

As stated above, the product of the z transforms of $1/(1 + s)$ and $2/(2 + s)$ is not $G(z)$.   If the z transform of $G(s)$ is not available in the table of z transforms, $G(s)$ must be expanded in partial fractions, each of which is transformable.

Thus, from Eqs. (8-44) and (8-45),

$$G(s) = \frac{A_1}{1 + s} + \frac{A_2}{2 + s}$$

$$A_1 = \lim_{s \to -1} \frac{2}{2 + s} = 2$$

$$A_2 = \lim_{s \to -2} \frac{2}{1 + s} = -2$$

Whence

$$G(s) = \frac{2}{1 + s} - \frac{2}{2 + s}$$

and from Table 9-1,

$$G(z) = \frac{2z}{z - e^{-T}} - \frac{2z}{z - e^{-2T}}$$

or

$$G(z) = \frac{2}{1 - z^{-1}e^{-T}} - \frac{2}{1 - z^{-1}e^{-2T}} \qquad (9\text{-}33)$$

The temporal response of a sampled-data system, or indeed of a continuous signal system at regular intervals of time, can be determined by inverse transformation of the z transform for the forced system. It can also be determined by expanding the z transform as a series in z^{-n}, because the coefficients on the z^{-n} terms will be the magnitudes of the system response at the times nT, where $n = 1, 2, 3, \ldots$. This characteristic follows directly from the fact that $z^{-n} = e^{-nTs}$, which is the Laplace transform for translation nT units along the time axis.

Example 9-5 Estimate the step response of a transfer stage with a time constant of 1 min by assuming that the system is a sampled-data one.

Solution The transfer function of this system is

$$\frac{C}{R}(s) = \frac{1}{1 + s}$$

and the forcing function is

$$R(s) = \frac{1}{s}$$

Whence

$$C(s) = \frac{1}{s(1 + s)} \qquad (9\text{-}34)$$

which may be expanded in partial fractions to

$$C(s) = \frac{1}{s} - \frac{1}{s + 1}$$

From Table 9-1, the z transform, term by term, is

$$C(z) = \frac{z}{z - 1} - \frac{z}{z - e^{-T}}$$

or

$$C(z) = \frac{z(1 - e^{-T})}{z^2 - z(1 + e^{-T}) + e^{-T}} \tag{9-35}$$

If we choose $T \cong 0.222$, $e^{-T} = 0.8000$, and Eq. (9-35) becomes

$$C(z) = \frac{0.2z}{z^2 - 1.8z + 0.8} \tag{9-36}$$

By synthetic division of the denominator into the numerator, there results

$$
\begin{array}{r}
0.2z^{-1} + 0.36z^{-2} + 0.49z^{-3} + \ \cdots \\
\hline
z - 1.8z + 0.8 \big) 0.2z \\
0.2z \quad - 0.36 \quad + 0.16z^{-1} \\
\hline
0.36 \quad + 0.16z^{-1} \\
0.36 \quad - 0.65z^{-1} + 0.288z^{-2} \\
\hline
0.49z^{-1} - 0.288z^{-2} \\
0.49z^{-1} - 0.882z^{-2} + 0.392z^{-3}
\end{array}
$$

and

$$C(z) = 0.2z^{-1} + 0.36z^{-2} + 0.49z^{-3} + 0.594z^{-4} + 0.678z^{-5}$$

$$+ 0.745z^{-6} + 0.800z^{-7} + \ \cdots \tag{9-37}$$

These terms are response pulses displaced in time T, $2T$, . . . , or in tabular form,

	$n = 1$	$n = 2$	$n = 3$	$n = 4$	$n = 5$	$n = 6$	$n = 7$
$t + 0.222n$	0.22	0.44	0.67	0.89	1.11	1.33	1.55
$c(t)$	0.20	0.36	0.49	0.59	0.68	0.74	0.80

The result of the foregoing example is identical at the sampling instants with that which would be obtained by direct inversion of the Laplace transform in Eq. (9-34). In general, the smaller the sampling interval T is set, the more surely one can interpolate the response between the sampling instants.

If the temporal response is obtained by inverse transforming of the z transform, the result is a continuous function of time which, at the sampling instants, is exactly the temporal response, but which, at other times, may not be equal to the temporal response.

9-13   Design of sampled-data control systems

Consider the simple regulator system shown in Fig. 9-11, in which the controlled variable is sensed by element B at sampling intervals of T sec. All other parts of the system function continuously, and H is a zero-order hold circuit.

If G is known and not subject to modification, the design problem is one of choosing G_c and B to accommodate the likely disturbances in U. Furthermore, if B has the dynamic characteristics of a pure time delay of T sec, the problem is reduced to that of specifying the sampling interval and the controller characteristics.

Subject to the condition that the cycle period of the sensing device be physically attainable, the sampling interval is chosen to be short enough to assure the transfer of sufficient information through the feedback loop. It can be shown (see Ragazzini and Franklin) that as much information can be carried by the z transform as can be carried by the Laplace transform if the frequency of sampling is at least twice that of the highest frequency of interest in the system.

For the system of Fig. 9-11, the highest frequencies of interest would depend on the nature of the disturbance signal U and the critical frequency of the closed-loop system. In typical process systems the range of important frequencies in the disturbances would lie well below the closed-loop frequencies, and hence the choice of sampling interval would be based on the critical frequency of the closed-loop system.

If the sampling frequency can be set higher than twice the open-loop critical frequency, the design methods for linear continuous systems based on the Laplace transform are entirely adequate. In this case the sampler in the feedback loop is treated as a pure time delay of T. On

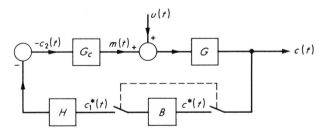

Figure 9-11   Regulator system with sampler in feedback.

the other hand, if the sampling frequency must be smaller, the design must make use of the z transform.

For the system of Fig. 9-11, the flow of signals around the loop is given in terms of Laplace transforms by the three equations

$$C^*(s) = BC^*(s) \tag{9-38}$$

$$C_2(s) = H_2^*(s) \tag{9-39}$$

$$C(s) = GU(s) - G_cGC_2(s) \tag{9-40}$$

The starred quantities are pulsed variables, and the B, H, and G are all functions of s.

Eliminating $C_1^*(s)$ and $C_2(s)$ from these equations and solving for $C(s)$, but only at the sampling instants when $C^*(s) = C(s)$ and $U(s) = U^*(s)$, gives

$$C^*(s) = \frac{GU^*(s)}{1 + G_cGHB} \tag{9-41}$$

and by z transformation,

$$C(z) = \frac{GU(z)}{1 + G_cGHB(z)} \tag{9-42}$$

where, for example, $GU(z)$ is the z transform of the product $G(s)U(s)$.

Equation (9-42) may be used for determining G_c by testing likely values for the parameters in G_c, such as K_p, T_I, and T_D, using some convenient and typical forcing in $U(z)$. The z transforms for the functions GU and G_cGHB must be determined by partial-fraction expansion of the corresponding Laplace transform. Inversion to the time domain may be effected either by resort to the transform table or by expansion of Eq. (9-42) as a series in z^{-nT}.

If the process transfer function G, or indeed any transfer function in the loop, contains a time delay $e^{-T_d s}$, the sampling interval should be set equal to T_d/k, where k is an integer. Then the substitution z^{-k} may be made for the time-delay transfer function when the transformation to Eq. (9-42) is made.

Problems

9-1 Show that the optimum controller for a liquid-flow control system is a proportional plus integral controller with low proportional gain and high reset rate.

9-2 For the process system defined by Fig. 9-5 and a desired damping factor in the closed-loop transient behavior of 0.04, what is the highest damped frequency attainable with a conventional proportional plus compensated rate controller?

9-3 The dynamics of a process system can be represented by a general plant characteristic consisting of a pure time delay of 8 sec, coupled to a first-order transfer lag with a time constant of 4 sec, and a second-order element for which the natural frequency is 0.2 rad/sec and the damping ratio is 0.8. Calculate the open-loop frequency-response characteristics for this system, assuming that the overall steady-state gain is unity. What proportional band would ensure stable control when the loop is closed through a proportional controller?

9-4 In the feedback system of Prob. 9-3, a disturbance equivalent in the steady state to ±15 percent of the controlled variable and with a period of 10 sec is imposed on the process at a point downstream from the delay and the first-order lag but upstream from the second-order element. How much can this disturbance be suppressed with proportional plus integral control?

9-5 A process system, including the final control elements and the sensing elements in open-loop array, is forced sinusoidally by the pneumatic signal to the control elements at a steady amplitude of 2 psig. The following data are obtained:

Frequency, rad/min	0	0.1	0.4	1.0	4.0
Output amplitude, °C	26	24	20	10	2
Phase lag, deg	0	40	100	180	360

It is proposed to control this system with a proportional controller which responds to signals over a temperature range of 0 to 100°C and which generates pneumatic signals over the range of 3 to 15 psig. A gain setting of 1.0 on the controller corresponds to a change in output of 12 psig for a 100° change in controller input. What minimum gain setting would be required to make the closed-loop system unstable?

9-6 A process plant may be characterized by an 8-sec time delay coupled to a second-order transfer lag with time constants of 10 and 20 sec. This plant is to be controlled with a proportional plus integral controller set to a gain margin of 2.5. The integral action is to be added only if the steady-state error for reference changes is greater than 5 percent, and its addition must not change the critical frequency of the system when the integral phase contribution is represented by the straight-line approximations. What controller characteristics do you recommend for this system?

9-7 For the system of Prob. 9-6, sketch the step response of the process alone, and from the rules of Ziegler and Nichols, estimate the required proportional gain and integral action. Compare the results with those obtained on Prob. 9-6.

9-8   Under normal conditions of operation, a simple but large fractionator is observed to have dynamic characteristics in respect to the response in overhead composition to forcing in the steam supply to the reboiler, approximating those of a 10-min time delay coupled to a first-order lag of 40 min.   A periodic composition meter using refractive index as measure of composition is available for product-composition monitoring at an operating period of 20 min.   Suggest a simple scheme for controlling this system by means of a continuous controller moderating the steam supply. What limitations would the controlled system have?

9-9   If a sampling sensor is used in the system of Prob. 9-6, what controller characteristics would you recommend for various sampling intervals, including the longest practicable interval?

complex control systems

If we define simple control systems as those linear systems which consist of a single loop with one controlled variable and one manipulated variable and for which the set point is either fixed or varies in a predictable manner, then, by implication, all other control systems are complex. In this chapter we examine some representative complex systems, including multiple-loop systems and multiple-variable systems. We consider the problems of nonlinearity and optimality, and we assess the possibilities of achieving the fully automatic process plant.

10-1   Multiple-loop control systems

The treatment of multiple-loop control systems poses no special problems so long as there is only one principal controlled variable and no other complications. By the use of block-diagram algebra the multiple-loop system can always be reduced to a single-loop system involving one forcing variable and one response variable.

10-2   Cascade control

A common and relatively simple example of a multiple-loop control system is one using cascade control. The distinguishing characteristic of cascade control is that the output of a primary, or master, controller is the set point for a secondary, or slave, controller. This type of control provides an effective means of dealing with certain kinds of disturbances or load changes.

Figure 10-1 shows a pipestill heater where the fuel-gas-flow rate to the burners is controlled by a cascade of two controllers. The master controller, in response to changes in the temperature of the oil leaving the heater, adjusts the set point of a flow controller in the fuel-gas line. This flow controller then holds the flow rate at the value called for by the master controller.

It is clear that this system could be controlled with a single controller, but it is equally clear that a single controller would not be well able to accommodate changes in the supply pressure of the fuel gas. Such a change would have to produce a change in the hot-oil temperature before any countervailing control action could take place. With

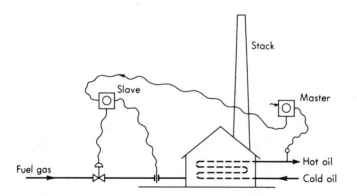

Figure 10-1   Pipestill heater with cascade control.

cascade control, on the other hand, the change in supply pressure would produce an immediate change in gas-flow rate and an equally swift controller response to hold the gas rate at the desired level. As a result, there would be no detectable change in the hot-oil temperature, which is the principal control variable.

It is instructive to compare the cascaded and uncascaded control systems. A block diagram of the signal flows for the system of Fig. 10-1 is shown in Fig. 10-2.

In this diagram R is the set point of the master controller, which has a transfer function G_c. The output from the master controller is the set point to the slave controller, identified by the transfer function G_{c_1}. Feedback elements are designated by the transfer functions H_1 for the gas-flow meter and H for the hot-oil thermometer. The final control elements for gas flow have the composite transfer function G_1, and the overall transfer function for the furnace and oil tubes is G. The disturbance input U is handled as an equivalent gas flow; C, the controlled variable, is the temperature of the hot oil leaving the heater.

For convenience in manipulation without any sacrifice in generality, we may assume that the instrument elements defined by G_1, H_1, and H contribute negligibly to the dynamic and the steady-state behavior of the system. The block diagram now may be drawn as in Fig. 10-3.

Since we are concerned here with the regulator problem rather than the servomechanism problem, we regard the system as being unperturbed in set point, and therefore $R = 0$. From the definition of an operational block,

$$M = G_c(-C) \tag{10-1}$$

$$M_1 = G_{c_1}(M - U - M_1) \tag{10-2}$$

$$C = G(U + M_1) \tag{10-3}$$

where M is the output of the master controller and the set point for the secondary controller, and M_1 is the output of the secondary controller.

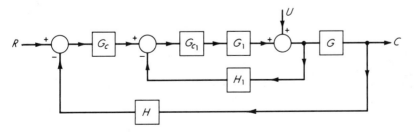

Figure 10-2   Signal-flow diagram for cascade control system.

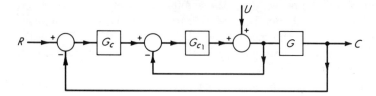

Figure 10-3   Simplified block diagram for cascade control.

Elimination of M and M_1 among these equations and rearrangement of the resulting expression gives

$$\left(\frac{C}{U}\right)_{\text{cascaded}} = \frac{G}{1 + G_{c_1} + G_c G_{c_1} G} \tag{10-4}$$

For the uncascaded control case the signal-flow diagram would be that given by Fig. 10-4, and the performance would be given by Eq. (10-5).

$$\left(\frac{C}{U}\right)_{\text{uncascaded}} = \frac{G}{1 + G_c G} \tag{10-5}$$

It can be seen that the effect of adding the cascaded control is to insert the slave-controller transfer function at two points in the denominator of the closed-loop transfer function. The result is a substantial decrease in the response of the controlled variable to disturbances.

The effect of cascade control on the stability of the closed-loop system can be gauged from the polynomial in the denominator of the closed-loop transfer function, namely,

$$1 + G_{c_1} + G_c G_{c_1} G = 0 \tag{10-6}$$

We may rearrange this equation into the form equivalent to the form implied in determining system stability from the open-loop frequency-response characteristic. Thus

$$G_c \frac{G_{c_1}}{1 + G_{c_1}} G = -1 \tag{10-7}$$

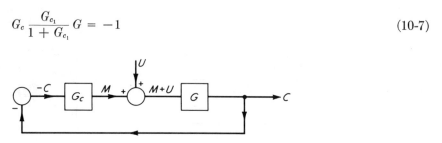

Figure 10-4   Simplified diagram for uncascaded control.

According to this equation, the limiting condition of stability obtains at the frequency for which the angle

$$\left/ G_c \frac{G_{c_1}}{1 + G_{c_1}} G \right. = -180°$$

when the magnitude

$$|G_c| \left| \frac{G_{c_1}}{1 + G_{c_1}} \right| |G| = \text{unity}$$

If the secondary loop (inner loop) is set for an acceptable level of stability, the maximum magnitude ratio for that loop will be about 1.20. This peak, however, will occur at a frequency far above those which are critical for the stability of the overall loop if the secondary loop is fast compared with the primary loop. At the critical frequency for the overall loop, the magnitude ratio of the secondary loop would be essentially unity, and the angle contribution would be very small.

The foregoing discussion has implied that certain features must be incorporated in cascade control systems. First of all, the secondary loop must involve the primary forcing variables of the system, and it must include the disturbance input. Indeed, it is advantageous to include as many disturbance inputs as can be accommodated without decreasing seriously the speed of the secondary loop. Second, the secondary loop should be much faster than the master loop. Some designers recommend speed ratios higher than 3, and preferably as high as 5, and even up to 10; that is, the characteristic frequencies for the secondary loop should exceed those of the primary loop by these factors.

10-3   Ratio control

Another fairly common and simple kind of a multiple-loop control system is one involving ratio control. In many process operations it is necessary to mix two or more constituents continuously to maintain a steady composition in the resulting mixture. A simple means of effecting this mixing is to use a conventional flow controller on one stream and control the other stream with a ratio controller which maintains that stream at some preset ratio to the primary stream flow.

A ratio control system for regulating the composition of a feed stream to a reactor wherein a hydrocarbon is partially oxidized by air is shown in Fig. 10-5. The signal-flow diagram for this system is shown in Fig. 10-6. In this diagram the subscript 1 refers to air and 2 refers to the hydrocarbon, and K is the ratio, which is adjustable.

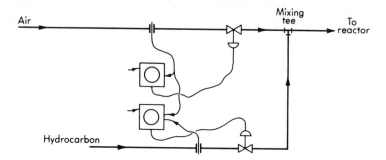

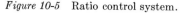

Figure 10-5   Ratio control system.

The design of ratio control systems poses no special problem since the loops may be designed separately, and the single-loop methods of design are applicable.

10-4   *Feedforward control*

It has been emphasized in earlier chapters that the feedback of signals is essential in all automatic control systems.   There are many systems, however, for which a feedforward of certain signals offers a valuable addition to the feedback loop.   In process sequences, for example, where elements downstream from other elements are necessarily subject to the perturbations in output signals from the upstream elements, it often is advantageous to feedforward information about these perturbations.

A simple example of a feedforward-feedback system is shown in Fig. 10-7.   The disturbing function U, in this case, might be a perturbation in the composition of a feed stream coming from a reactor and into a separation system.   If the disturbances are large, a satisfactory design for the separation system would be to include a measurement of the disturbing signal via G_F and an auxiliary control manipulation via G_{CF}. The desired properties in G_F and G_{CF} may be identified readily by writing the system transfer function C/U.   Thus, for $R = 0$,

$$\frac{C}{U} = \frac{G(1 - G_{CF}G_FG_1)}{1 + HG_cG_1G} \tag{10-8}$$

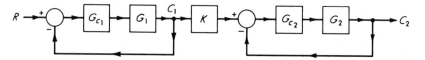

Figure 10-6   Signal-flow diagram for ratio control.

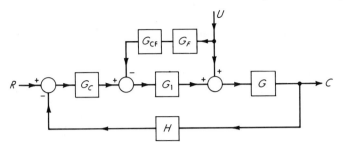

Figure 10-7 Feedforward-feedback control system.

and for zero response in C to perturbations U,

$$G_{\text{CF}}G_F = \frac{1}{G_1} \qquad (10\text{-}9)$$

Since G_F is the transfer function of some kind of sensing element and G_1 is the transfer function of a valve and its actuator, the matching specifications for the auxiliary-controller transfer function G_{CF} might have to include differentiating action. For example, if the sensor behaved as a first-order element with a time constant of the same order of magnitude as typical periods in the disturbing function, and if the dynamics of G_1 were too rapid to have a deleterious influence, G_{CF} would be a proportional plus derivative control function, with the proportional gain equal to the steady-state gain of $(G_F G_1)^{-1}$.

The design of the principal loop for this system is the same as for a simple single-loop system. An inspection of Eq. (10-8) shows that the system may be regarded as a single-loop system if the disturbing function is fed into the summer through an element with a transfer function of $1 - G_{\text{CF}}G_F G_1$. Hence the stability analysis of the main loop can be made without including the properties of the subsidiary loop. Figure 10-8 shows the block diagram for this treatment.

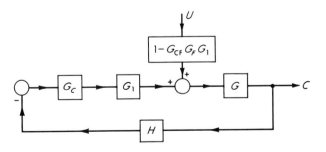

Figure 10-8 System of Fig. 10-7 as single-loop system.

10-5   *Multiple-variable systems*

Our treatment of control systems so far has been limited to systems for which there is only one principal forcing variable and one principal response variable. Most process systems are forced by more than one variable, and there is, generally, more than one output signal. Nevertheless, an adequate treatment of the control problem is possible on the assumption that only one output signal and one input signal are of overriding importance. For example, as in the system of Fig. 10-9, a chemical reactor wherein a hydrocarbon vapor in air is oxidized over a catalyst might be subject to four or more significant forcing signals and have an equal number of response signals. The input signals would include the total gas-flow rate to the reactor, the gas composition and temperature, and the coolant-flow rate and temperature. The output signals would include the gas-outflow composition and temperature and the coolant exit temperature. A simple procedure for the design of the control instrumentation for this system would be to control the principal variables separately. The total gas flow would be subject to approximate control by regulating the flow of the air, which typically would be the preponderant material in the feed gas. The concentration of the hydrocarbon vapor in the feed would be held constant by conventional control of the flow of hydrocarbon into the airstream. A safer alternative would be to regulate the hydrocarbon-flow rate to maintain a fixed ratio of hydrocarbon to air flow as described in Sec. 10-3.

The temperature of the feed gas would be regulated to a constant level by a simple heat exchanger external to the reactor. With all the foregoing key forcing variables under reasonably tight control, the final control of the reactor itself would involve nothing more than regulating

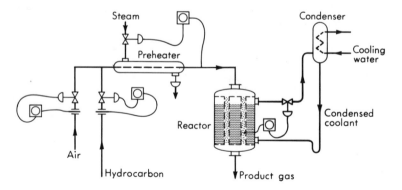

Figure 10-9   Multivariable control system.

the temperature level in the reactor by manipulating the flow rate and initial temperature of the reactor coolant. If the coolant were a boiling liquid, the only quantity to manipulate would be the boiling pressure.

The control system which results from the foregoing design procedure may involve more instrumentation hardware than is absolutely necessary, but with adequate sizing of the reactor and cooling system, the control would be sure. In effect what is done is to make successive appraisals of the control system in terms of each possible pair of forcing and response variables. For most process systems only a very few pairs of variables will be important, and often these can be identified by inspection.

If we confine our treatment of the system to the case of small perturbations about particular operating levels, the effects of all the forcings on a particular response variable will be additive. Thus we can compute the total response for any combination of simultaneous forcings. Figure 10-10 shows this characteristic on a signal-flow diagram. The forcing signals are designated R_i, and the response is C. For this system

$$C = R_1G_1 + R_2G_2 + R_3G_3 \tag{10-10}$$

The general analytical treatment of the linear multivariable system requires the use of matrix algebra, and the resulting stability equation involves matrices corresponding to sets of stability equations. Both analog and digital computers can accommodate this problem readily in principle. The difficulty of accommodation in practice increases rapidly with the number of variables.

10-6 Nonlinear systems

It is instructive at this point to examine briefly what may be done to deal with systems which do not behave linearly. For the purposes of this treatment we distinguish two kinds of nonlinearities, namely, continuous and discontinuous nonlinearities.

Continuous nonlinearities, sometimes called progressive nonlineari-

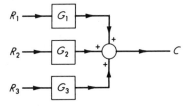

Figure 10-10 Linear multiple-variable system.

ties, occur when the response is a monotonic but nonlinear function of the forcing. A familiar and simple example is the case of flow through an orifice where the flow rate is proportional to the square root of the pressure drop across the orifice.

Discontinuous nonlinearities are those for which the response is a discontinuous function of the forcing. In process control systems they result principally from saturation, backlash, and coulomb friction, all of which effects are found in valves.

Saturation occurs, for example, when an undersized valve reaches the fully opened position. Further control action to open the valve has no effect on the flow through the valve, which is already at maximum rate. On-off control action is inherently saturated since the valve typically goes from fully open to fully closed positions.

Backlash is the condition which obtains when there is play in mechanical parts so that there is no response for small forcing signals. The result is a dead zone in the system.

Coulomb friction also causes a dead zone in the system response characteristics. In process valves this condition commonly arises from the tendency of the valve stem to stick in the packing, which seals the valve. The forcing signal must exceed some threshold increment before the valve will move.

Continuous nonlinearities may be handled quite readily by linearization and the use of linear procedures when the operating system is subject to mild excursions about fixed operating points.

Under conditions where there are large excursions of the process variables, such as occur during plant startup, the linear procedures are not reliably applicable, and other methods must be used.

The most straightforward approach is to simulate the system on a large-scale analog or digital computer. For rapid determination of the effects of various system parameters, the analog computer is particularly useful: it can accommodate nonlinearities and also multiple variables and multiple loops. For systems of any great complexity, the capability requirements for either analog or digital computation can be quite formidable, and considerable ingenuity and skill born of experience are necessary to reduce and simplify the analysis to a tractable level.

If the transfer functions for the systems are known at all operating levels encountered in the course of the startup, it is possible to design the control elements to ensure stability. The procedure is to specify control-element characteristics which will make the system stable for linear-range perturbations at all operating levels involved in the startup. Then, as a consequence of a dictum attributed to Liapunov, the system cannot be unstable in the face of large (nonlinear-range) perturbations.

Continuous nonlinearities may also be treated by the describing function (Sec. 10-7) and by phase-plane analysis (Sec. 10-8).

Discontinuous nonlinearities may be treated by the describing function as well as by computer, but the simplest approach is to solve the problem directly by mechanical means. Saturation may be eliminated by the proper sizing of system elements; backlash may be reduced by the replacement of worn mechanical elements; and coulomb friction may be overcome by the use of *dither*, which is the application of a low-amplitude oscillatory signal to maintain a continuing but slight movement in mechanical parts, and thereby prevent sticking.

10-7 Describing function

For systems with one nonlinear element coupled in series with a number of linear elements, the convenience of frequency-response analysis may be realized by means of the describing function. The response of the nonlinear element to sustained sinusoidal forcing will be a distorted sinusoid, with the fundamental frequency equal to the forcing frequency, but with higher-frequency components also contributing to the response. By a Fourier analysis on the response waveform, it is possible to identify the fundamental component, and the ratio of this component to the forcing sinusoid is the describing function. This function will define a magnitude ratio and a phase angle just as for a linear element, but these quantities now are functions, not only of the frequency, but also of the amplitude of the forcing signal.

The linear elements following the nonlinear element will exert a filtering action on the higher-harmonic components in the distorted waveform emerging from the nonlinear element. In general, the attenuation of these higher harmonics in the linear elements will eliminate their contribution to the system dynamics. As a result, we may use conventional frequency-response techniques for the design of systems which contain a single nonlinear element in series with linear elements. The describing function gives the effective frequency-response characteristics of the nonlinear element. An appropriate amplitude, or range of amplitudes, must be chosen for the signal entering the nonlinear element.

10-8 Phase-plane analysis

If a control system is describable by a nonlinear equation of the form

$$\frac{d^2x}{dt^2} + f_1\left(x, \frac{dx}{dt}\right)\frac{dx}{dt} + f_2\left(x, \frac{dx}{dt}\right)x = 0 \qquad (10\text{-}11)$$

it is possible to use phase-plane analysis to identify the response to various kinds of forcings.

The phase plane is the mapping surface on which the ordinate is dx/dt and the abscissa is x. A plot of all possible paths of dx/dt versus x on this plane for a particular system is called the phase portrait of the system. In general, there will be a different path for different initial conditions. Although time is not explicitly identified on these plots, it is possible to estimate the temporal response of the system by a simple graphical integration.

The direction of a particular path on the phase plane reveals the stability of the system for particular initial conditions. If the plot runs off to infinity with increasing time, the system is unstable. If the plot describes a closed figure which repeats itself continually over time, the system will undergo sustained oscillations, called limit cycles.

The limit cycle is a characteristic of nonlinear systems. It is the condition observed when the controller on a process control system is tuned in the field by raising the controller gain until the system undergoes a sustained oscillation. If the system were truly linear, it would not be possible to set the gain so precisely that the cycling would not change in amplitude. The fact that a sustained oscillation can be obtained is directly attributable to one or more nonlinearities in the system.

In experienced hands the phase-plane analysis is a convenient and powerful technique, but its usefulness in dealing with nonlinear systems is limited to the class of systems describable by equations of the form of (10-11). Phase-plane representation is quite applicable to linear second-order systems, although it offers no great advantage over other linear techniques.

10-9   *Liapunov function*

Many of the recent developments in dealing with nonlinear systems have been based on the work in applied mechanics of Liapunov, at the turn of the century. Liapunov devised two methods of stability analysis, each applicable in principle to both linear and nonlinear systems. The first method is based on the analytical solution of the system equations, and hence is of limited utility. The second, or direct, method is based on a qualitative approach in which a particular scalar function of the system properties is sought. If such a function, called a Liapunov function, is found, the system is stable. If a function cannot be found, the system may yet be stable, inasmuch as a further search might identify the Liapunov function.

Since the search for a Liapunov function is similar in many respects to the search for an analytical solution of the system equations, there are virtually no useful generalities for nonlinear systems at the present time, although many workers are concerned with the problem. The interested reader is referred to the book of La Salle and Lefschetz.

10-10 Computer control

For some systems it may be advantageous to incorporate in the control system, in addition to the conventional sensors, controller, and final control elements, some kind of computer which would provide a better measure of the controlled condition in the system or which would generate a control action based on a more realistic appraisal of the objectives of the control system. Such systems are called computer control systems, although in a strict sense all the control systems we have considered heretofore are computer control systems, since conventional controllers may be regarded as computers. Conventional controllers contain analog computing elements which add, multiply by a constant, integrate, and differentiate signals.

Among the simpler types of computer control systems are those in which signals derived from two or more measured process variables are fed to an analog computing element which determines from these variables a property of the system that is more directly a measure of the balance in the system than is any measurable property. A common example of this type of system is a fractionator control system based on column heat balance.

An important type of computer control system is the self-optimizing, or optimalizing, control system. A relatively simple example is the fractionator for which an economically optimum operation is specified to effect a compromise between the cost of reboiler steam and the incremental improvement in products value over feed value. The computer calculates the economic advantage at a given operating level, and then directs the system in a hunt for a better operating level. The jumps from one operating level to another cover a preset interval and a preset sequence of directions. Each time a hunting sequence identifies a new optimal operating level, that level becomes the base for the next hunting sequence.

Adaptive control is the name given to the kind of optimizing control in which it is necessary to adjust controller characteristics, for example, to accommodate changes in process characteristics. A typical case would be a sensitive chemical reactor which requires a precise optimized dynamic behavior but which has a catalyst with a high rate of decline in activity. The computer for this system would have to set optimum controller settings on the basis of catalyst activity.

10-11   Unmanageable systems

Central computer control also has an important potential in the control of processes which are uncontrollable by conventional means. One example would be a polymerization process involving highly nonlinear chemical kinetics wherein the desired product has to meet rigid specifications as to average molecular weight and distribution of polymer chain lengths. Up to the present time there has been little economic incentive to develop the controls for such systems because development funds could usually be expended more profitably for other processes or process improvements. With tighter competition and the availability of greatly improved instruments for monitoring product quality, however, there will be increased advantages in harnessing processes which in times past could not be developed because they were unmanageable.

10-12   Fully automatic plant

There are no inherent barriers to putting into operation a fully automatic optimized plant. Modern digital computers are capable of handling enormous volumes of information extremely rapidly. One machine in central control of a process plant could analyze all the information pertinent to the operation of the plant, including not only information about process variables, but also information about selling prices of products and the cost and quality of raw materials. On the basis of continuing analyses of the plant's behavior, the central computer could devise a mathematical model of the entire plant, and for any observed disturbance or forcing signal to the plant, the computer could determine quickly from the model just what kinds of control action should be taken to maintain an economically optimum performance.

Some plants of moderate complexity, including those for manufacturing ammonia and ethylene and for fractionating crude oil, are being controlled in this manner by central computers. In these plants a central digital computer manipulates the set points of conventional process controllers. An important advantage of this arrangement is that a failure of the central computer would not necessitate a shutdown of the plant. The major disadvantage is that the central computer generally has ample capacity for computing the individual controller actions, and hence the investment in the individual control instruments is unnecessary. Continuing improvements in the operating efficiencies, that is, in the length of on-stream time before failure, of digital computers probably will lead, ultimately, to the elimination of the individual process controllers for many types of systems. Indeed, this elimination is already feasible for plants sufficiently large to warrant investment in a second, backup computer.

Theoretically, the same principles which permit the use of computer control in individual process plants can be extended to include complex integrated plants, whole works and refineries, and even entire corporate enterprises consisting of many manufacturing plants and related operations. In practice, this extension presents formidable difficulties in the acquisition, evaluation, and processing of the relevent process and economic data, but all current trends are clearly in this direction.

Problems

10-1   Suggest an instrumentation scheme for a fractional distillation system consisting of a 20-deck tower, a water-cooled condenser, a steam-heated reboiler, and a steam-heated preheater for the feed stream. The feed stream is a liquid binary mixture entering on the seventh tray from the top. Its composition is constant in time, but its flow rate changes occasionally by as much as 10 percent. The product streams are an overhead stream from the condenser and a bottom stream from the reboiler. There is a rapidly responsive composition sensor in the vapor line from the top of the column, which provides the controlled variable signal for regulating the flow rate of liquid reflux from the condenser to the top tray of the tower.

For this problem use only conventional controllers and simple feedback loops. Identify all assumptions and indicate the possible shortcomings of your design.

10-2   Repeat Prob. 10-1 using cascaded control and ratio control to improve the design but without any feedforward sequences. Identify all assumptions and indicate the shortcomings of your design. Note that reflux ratio, the ratio of liquid downflow to vapor upflow in the upper section of the tower, determines the overhead product purity.

10-3   Repeat Prob. 10-1 using feedforward as well as cascade and ratio control. *Hint:* Measure the feed-stream-flow rate and relate both the reflux rate and the reboiler-stream rate to this measure.

10-4   In climates where cooling water is expensive, it is often economically advantageous to use air-cooled condensers in fractional distillation systems. The condensers are controlled by regulating the flow of air past their finned tubes. Unfortunately large changes in ambient air temperatures can produce large changes in reflux temperatures with the result that the internal reflux in the column will change even though the reflux to the top tray (external reflux) remains constant. Suggest a simple computer control system to ensure accurate manipulation of the internal reflux. *Hint:* Make an enthalpy balance around the top tray using measured temperatures of the external reflux and the liquid leaving the tray (internal reflux).

10-5   Suggest a simple computer control scheme for the system of Prob. 10-1 which would permit elimination of the feed preheater.

selected bibliography

A Mathematics

1 Abramowitz, M., and I. A. Stegun (eds.): "Handbook of Mathematical Functions," National Bureau of Standards, Washington, D.C., 1964.

2 Bellman, R., and R. Kalaba (eds.): "Selected Papers on Mathematical Trends in Control Theory," Dover Publications, Inc., New York, 1964.

3 Churchill, R. V.: "Complex Variables and Applications," 2d ed., McGraw-Hill Book Company, New York, 1960.

4 Churchill, R. V.: "Operational Mathematics," 2d ed., McGraw-Hill Book Company, New York, 1958.

5 Gardner, M. F., and J. L. Barnes: "Transients in Linear Systems," John Wiley & Sons, Inc., New York, 1942.

6 Jensen, V. G., and G. V. Jeffreys: "Mathematical Methods in Chemical Engineering," Academic Press Inc., New York, 1963.

7 Lapidus, L.: "Digital Computation for Chemical Engineers," McGraw-Hill Book Company, New York, 1962.

8 Mickley, H. S., T. K. Sherwood, and C. E. Reed: "Applied Mathematics in Chemical Engineering," 2d ed., McGraw-Hill Book Company, New York, 1957.

B Control theory, general

1 Brown, G. S., and D. P. Campbell: "Principles of Servomechanisms," John Wiley & Sons, Inc., New York, 1948.

2 Chestnut, H., and R. W. Mayer: "Servomechanism and Regulating System Design," vols. 1 and 2, John Wiley & Sons, Inc., New York, 1951–1955.

3 Draper, C. S., W. McKay, and S. Lees: "Instrument Engineering," vol. 1, Fundamentals, vol. 2, Mathematics, McGraw-Hill Book Company, New York, 1952–1953.

4 Evans, W. R.: "Control System Dynamics," McGraw-Hill Book Company, New York, 1954.

5 Gille, J. C., M. J. Pelegrin, and P. Decaulne: "Feedback Control Systems," McGraw-Hill Book Company, New York, 1959.

6 Grabbe, E. M., S. Ramo, and D. E. Wooldridge (eds.): "Handbook of Automation, Computation and Control," vol. 1, "Control Fundamentals," vol. 2, "Computers and Data Processing," vol. 3, "Systems and Components," John Wiley & Sons, Inc., New York, 1958–1961.

7 Graham, D., and D. McRuer: "Analysis of Nonlinear Control Systems," John Wiley & Sons, Inc., New York, 1961.

8 Horowitz, I. M.: "Synthesis of Feedback Systems." Academic Press Inc., New York, 1963.

9 Laning, J. H., Jr., and R. H. Battin: "Random Processes in Automatic Control," McGraw-Hill Book Company, New York, 1956.

10 La Salle, J., and S. Lefschetz: "Stability by Liapunov's Direct Method," Academic Press Inc., New York, 1961.

11 Leondes, C. T. (ed.): "Computer Control Systems Technology," McGraw-Hill Book Company, New York, 1961.

12 Oldenbourg, R. C., and H. Sartorius: "The Dynamics of Automatic Control," American Society of Mechanical Engineers, New York, 1948.

13 Oldenburger, R.: "Frequency Response," The Macmillan Company, New York, 1956.

14 Popov, E. P.: "The Dynamics of Automatic Control Systems," Addison-Wesley Publishing Company, Inc., Reading, Mass., 1962.

15 Ragazzini, J. R., and G. F. Franklin: "Sampled Data Control Systems," McGraw-Hill Book Company, New York, 1958.

16   Smith, O. J. M.: "Feedback Control Systems," McGraw-Hill Book Company, New York, 1958.

17   Tou, J. T.: "Optimum Design of Digital Control Systems," Academic Press Inc., New York, 1963.

18   Truxal, J. G.: "Automatic Feedback Control System Synthesis," McGraw-Hill Book Company, New York, 1955.

19   Truxal, J. G. (ed.): "Control Engineers' Handbook," McGraw-Hill Book Company, New York, 1958.

20   Tsien, H. S.: "Engineering Cybernetics," McGraw-Hill Book Company, New York, 1954.

21   Tustin, A. (ed.): "Automatic and Manual Control," Academic Press Inc., New York, 1952.

22   Zadeh, L. A., and C. A. Desoer: "Linear System Theory," McGraw-Hill Book Company, New York, 1963.

C   *Process control*

1   Buckley, P. S.: "Techniques of Process Control," John Wiley & Sons, Inc., New York, 1964.

2   Caldwell, W. I., G. A. Coon, and L. M. Zoss: "Frequency Response for Process Control," McGraw-Hill Book Company, New York, 1959.

3   Ceaglske, N. H.: "Automatic Process Control for Chemical Engineers," John Wiley & Sons, Inc., New York, 1956.

4   Coughanowr, D. R., and L. B. Koppel: "Process Systems Analysis and Control," McGraw-Hill Book Company, New York, 1965.

5   Eckman, D. P.: "Automatic Process Control," John Wiley & Sons, Inc., New York, 1958.

6   Farrington, G. H.: "Fundamentals of Automatic Control," John Wiley & Sons, Inc., New York, 1951.

7   Harriott, P.: "Process Control," McGraw-Hill Book Company, New York, 1964.

8   Perlmutter, D. D.: "Introduction to Chemical Process Control," John Wiley & Sons, Inc., New York, 1965.

9   Roberts, S. M.: "Dynamic Programming in Chemical Engineering and Process Control," Academic Press Inc., New York, 1964.

10   Williams, T. J.: "Systems Engineering for the Process Industries," McGraw-Hill Book Company, New York, 1961.

11   Young, A. J.: "Introduction to Process Control Systems Design," Longmans, Green & Co., Inc., New York, 1955.

D   *Process dynamics*

1   Campbell, D. P.: "Process Dynamics," John Wiley & Sons, Inc., New York, 1958.

2 Carslaw, H. J., and J. C. Jaeger: "Heat Conduction in Solids," 2d ed., Oxford University Press, Fair Lawn, N.J., 1959.

3 Society of Instrument Technology: "Plant and Process Dynamic Characteristics," Butterworth Scientific Publications, London, 1957.

4 Trimmer, J. D.: "Response of Physical Systems," John Wiley & Sons, Inc., New York, 1950.

E Instruments

1 Carroll, G. C.: "Industrial Process Measuring Instruments," McGraw-Hill Book Company, New York, 1962.

2 Draper, C. S., W. McKay, and S. Lees: "Instrument Engineering," vol. 3, pt. I, Measurement Systems, McGraw-Hill Book Company, New York, 1955.

3 Eckman, D. P.: "Industrial Instrumentation," John Wiley & Sons, Inc., New York, 1951.

4 Herzfeld, C. M. (ed.-in-chief): "Temperature: Its Measurement and Control in Science and Industry," vol. 3, F. G. Brickwedde (ed.), Basic Concepts, Standards and Methods, pt. 1, Reinhold Publishing Corporation, New York, 1962.

5 Pirani, M., and J. Yarwood: "Principles of Vacuum Engineering," Chapman & Hall, Ltd., London, 1961.

6 Rose-Innes, A. C.: "Low Temperature Techniques," D. Van Nostrand Company, Inc., Princeton, N.J., 1964.

F Articles cited in text

1 Boxer, R., and S. Thaler: A Simplified Method of Solving Linear and Nonlinear Systems," *Proc. IRE*, **44**:89 (1956).

2 Cohen, W. C., and E. F. Johnson: Distributed Parameter Process Dynamics, *Chem. Eng. Progr. Symp. Ser.* 36, **57**:86 (1961).

3 Smith, O. J. M.: Closer Control of Loops with Dead Time, *Chem. Eng. Progr.*, **53**:217 (1957).

4 Stermole, F. J., and M. A. Larson: Dynamic Response of Heat Exchangers to Flow Rate Changes, *Ind. Eng. Chem. Fundamentals*, **2**(1):62–67 (1963).

5 Ziegler, J. G., and N. B. Nichols: Optimum Settings for Automatic Controllers, *Trans. ASME*, **64**:759 (1942).

G Review

1 Williams, T. J.: Computers, Automation, and Process Control—Annual Review, *Ind. Eng. Chem.*, **56**(11):47–56 (November, 1964); **57**(12):33–43 (December, 1965); **58**(12):55–70 (December, 1966).

index

)t   Due